The Unguarded Moment

The Unguarded Moment

A Surgeon's Discovery of the
Barriers to Prescription of Inexpensive,
Effective Healthcare in the Form
of Therapeutic Exercise

Vert Mooney, M.D.

VANTAGE PRESS
New York

The opinions and instructions expressed herein are solely those of the author. Each individual should seek the advice of his or her own physician before starting any new medical program.

Cover design by Susan Thomas

FIRST EDITION

Published by Vantage Press, Inc.
419 Park Ave. South, New York, NY 10016

Manufactured in the United States of America
ISBN: 978-0-533-15584-2

Library of Congress Catalog Card No.: 2006906587

0 9 8 7 6 5 4 3

Contents

Preface

The purpose of this book is to emphasize the role of progressive resistance exercises, which can alter and delay the aging process. As a well-trained and experienced orthopaedic surgeon, I didn't understand this until recently. Once understood, the idea of progressive resistance exercises along with other positive lifestyle changes is so credible that one wonders why all of medicine doesn't embrace it. It's so simple. It's so cheap. That is why I felt it was necessary to write this book.

If I detailed my own education as to the value of progressive resistance exercises and the role of rational physical therapy, I could provide a convincing story. I was really not searching for a new answer. It emerged in a series of unguarded moments. In an effort to make the story more interesting and to supply context concerning the credibility of the concept, I feel it is necessary to weave some history of its development into the story. We all understand that pure therapeutic exercise is boring. Some way to spice up the story is necessary. An easy gimmick is to string it along the chronology of my own life of discovery. It's the personalities in life which make the journey so interesting. Many of these personalities that I was fortunate enough to stumble upon did, indeed, change the course of events. Indeed, that is the story of our culture. How a good idea can smoulder for a while and then burst into the flame of enthusiasm is a marvel. What is a fascinating subject to one person may seem to be as bland as white paint to another.

It's my fear that this mundane subject of the value of exercise will seem so self-evident that further education as to its role will not keep the reader's interest. It is my hope that the unusual personalities you meet along the way will keep you looking for more.

Many of the personalities discussed in this book will be unknown to the general reader. Once you see their impact, you will understand why they deserve more credit than, in general, the world has afforded them. Perhaps this small story can enlarge their impact on history.

The title "unguarded moment" also describes the human event of musculoskeletal injury and degeneration. We don't plan to have that sprained ankle or the backache which emerges when we bend down to pick up the newspaper. Perhaps if our nervous systems were more prepared, we could have avoided the event. On many occasions, such as the rear end motor vehicle accident, or being struck by an unseen player on the other team, nothing we could have done could have prevented it. We don't know how to prevent the wear and tear changes in our tissues called degeneration.

It is the combination of these two events of timing, the unguarded moment of injury and the unguarded moment of the surprises of personal education, which sets the stage for the following discussion. Education usually emerges through a series of unexpected events which illuminate our experience and, when appropriate, modify our views. Trauma and degeneration of our joints and soft tissues usually occur unexpectedly and likewise alter our lives.

Another reason for this book is to share with my children the events that I never had the time to relate. During the growth of my career, I was intensely involved with my work. As is often the case, the children grew up without much of a father's presence. I missed many opportunities to participate in their growth and enjoy the personal marvel of personality development of my own progeny. It is only thanks to the steady hand, intelligence and love of my dear wife, Ruth, that they have turned out so well. I am proud of them. I hope that the following reading can offset some of the loss of my interface with their growth. It may be, however, that my relative absence was better in the long run. My presence may have even deterred their successful maturity. We'll see as the story progresses.

The Unguarded Moment

1

The Problem

Why is it necessary to write a book about the development of therapeutic exercise? The simple answer is that current nonoperative care for soft tissue injury and degeneration is not based on objective measurement and thus reproducible concepts. This is especially true of back and neck pain. Because of that, many mystical and irrational mechanisms of pain control have emerged. That comment brings up the two core issues in our discussion—pain control and credibility.

Throughout this discussion, I will focus on the care of the common human experience of pain following soft tissue injuries. By soft tissue injuries, I mean trauma to our connective tissues—ligaments, joint capsules, muscles and tendons—and not the bones. Thanks to the discovery by Roentgen, for which he won the Nobel Prize in 1901, what were originally called "X-rays" have given surgeons marvelous insight when things go wrong with the bones and joints. Once the fractured bone can be identified, alignment can be corrected and, with modern surgical techniques, union of the fractured fragments in near anatomic realignment can be achieved. Excellent surgical repair of fractures is a fairly recent development and is some of the cause of the distraction that occurs to the orthopedic surgeon as he/she approaches a skeletal injury with the knowledge that it is fixable with appropriate surgery. There often is little thought of what should happen with the rest of the body. More important than that is the feedback of efficacy provided by follow-up X-rays, which can document the success of surgery and the eventual union. Also, when things go wrong for various technical reasons, X-rays can point the way to correction.

Such is not the case for the back strain, the whiplash injury and the finger and arm pain after days of typing. There are few objective signposts to define the dimension of the problem. There is no objective measure to monitor the efficacy of treatment. Our more recent radiographic insight into disturbed anatomy—the magnetic resonance imaging (MRI)—will show degenerating tissue but this finding cannot certainly indicate that tissue to be the source of pain. Degeneration of the soft tissues occurs with aging as surely as gray hair and lines on the face. Like those two attributes of continuing life experience, the impact of soft tissue degeneration is quite variable among us. Some people seem never to age and never even have gray hair. Others, for reasons only under the control of their parents and thousands of years of heritage, deteriorate more rapidly. The point is, this tissue deterioration/degeneration need be no more painful than the emerging lines on our faces, which document the passing birthdays.

It seems reasonable that medical science should be making progress to clarify the mystery of pain secondary to soft tissue injury and degeneration. This is especially important when it becomes a chronic problem. As will be discussed, the economic impact of chronic pain is a major societal problem in all of the civilized world. Who pays for this continued pain which apparently deters productive life? That word "apparently" is purposely placed. We all are aware that some of the payment for continued disability is based on mere statements by previously injured individuals who find this disability an opportunity to escape from an unpleasant work situation or some social or marital situation. Also, if you say you are in pain long enough and often enough, people will believe you. You will even begin to believe it.

Why Isn't It Fixed?

In that this is obviously a problem of significant financial importance, one would think that medical schools would have huge research products focused at improved understanding. But they don't. In that soft tissue pain is seldom life-threatening, or even results in a destructive disease process, much of medical science is focused on the preservation of human life—quite understandably. Moreover, pain is an area which falls somewhat between the crevices of medical turf. Although the psychologists and psychiatrists are describing the emotional sources of pain, and the molecular biologists are describing the chemical nature of the inflammatory process, the mutual understanding of these two areas often does not occur, nor is there good communication between the multiple flavors of medical clinicians who treat soft tissue pain.

Some years ago, when I was a professor in the Orthopedic Department of the University of California at San Diego, I was appointed to a committee which was to review the medical curriculum. As prologue to the committee work, the assistant dean in charge of the project reported to us a recent survey carried out by the American Association of Medical Colleges. This was a questionnaire which was sent out in a random manner to a significant portion of the fourth-year, soon-to-be-graduating medical students regarding their areas of competency. They were given a list of thirty-five different areas of medical care and asked to indicate their levels of self-perceived competence. The areas presented were the usual subjects of medical school, ranging from obstetrics to dermatology. There were two areas which the majority of medical students declared themselves least competent. They were 1) rehabilitation and 2) nutrition. Of course, these are the two areas over which we have the most control. They are the two areas, however, in which the documentation of efficacy of treatment is most limited.

In the area of nutrition, we are now going through what would seem to be a reversal of the recommendations of only a few years ago. Then there was an enthusiasm for carbohydrates and concern about too many fats and proteins. Now a new concept emerges where carbohydrates are considered a problem and some types of fat and protein are to be encouraged. A new type of diet appears on the bookshelves at almost monthly intervals. This is because there are so many factors at work related to nutrition that it is quite difficult to carry out studies which will give definitive answers. A more significant factor probably is at a financial level. Much of the current research is carried out by both government and industry. To carry out appropriate nutritional research, extremely large numbers of individuals have to be involved. To provide appropriate end points, it must be carried out for periods of time which may have to be measured in decades. This is extremely costly. The success of a researcher's career cannot be measured decades later. After all, preservation of life is the best measure of better nutrition. For their professional advancement, they need more or less immediate record of achievement.

Moreover, it is difficult for an industry to carry out such expensive research, which might offer a significant benefit for a specific product, different from theirs. Certainly, we are all aware of massive advertising related to the benefit of various food products, but this is largely uncontrolled and, although earnestly presented, is seldom substantiated by evidence in the scientific sense.

Essentially the same problem exists in the area of rehabilitation. In this sense, we are talking about the resolution of chronic disability secondary to injury and degeneration. As noted earlier, the problem is not life-threatening. What researcher would benefit from resolution of the problem? When it comes to government-sponsored research, it is organized under the umbrella of evidence-based research. To achieve the level of evidence-based research, the problem being treated has to be objectively identified so that all reviewing parties agree as to the definition. Many of the sources of pain secondary to degeneration and injury come from unverifiable anatomic sources. X-rays and MRIs do not show the abnormality. Physical examination often shows only diffuse tenderness and limitation of range of motion. The exact anatomic location of the abnormality cannot be determined. Lacking that clear definition, it is often difficult to be secure that all subjects in a particular study group really have the same abnormality.

Worse than that, however, is the lack of standardized measurable treatment applied to the soft tissue ailment, such as chronic recurrent back pain. Manipulation is not measurable, nor is massage. The impact of various modalities, such as heat, cold and electrical energy such as ultrasound really have not been measured. Individuals respond quite differently to each one of these sources of stimuli. In fact, that is the core of our ignorance in rational therapeutics for chronic soft tissue pain. If a study cannot define the dose of treatment, it is difficult to indicate that the treatment described was uniform and consistent.

An example of such an acceptance of this ridiculous reality is a recent study in Sweden, comparing surgery to nonoperative care for chronic recurrent back pain. The arrangement of the study certainly conformed to the ideal for appropriate clinical studies. The subjects of the study were randomized into four groups. They all had the same clinical problems. In this study, one group was the nonoperative group and the other three groups were randomized to three different types of spine fusion surgery. Fusion surgery is currently considered the ultimate solution for pain secondary to chronic degenerative disc disease. When the paper was presented, it was noted that the nonoperative care was "typical Swedish physical therapy", which included various types of exercise, massage, manipulation and heat and cold as considered appropriate by the treating therapist. Everybody got something different. The dose was impossible to determine. Worse than that was the fact that, in the study randomization process, while three quarters of the group were randomized to one of the three techniques of fusion surgery, the fourth group was randomized to the same type of treatment that they had failed to become candidates for this study. Not surprisingly, those receiving continued, ineffective, nonoperative care did not do as well as those receiving surgery. Nothing in the physical therapy group was measured. It should be noted also that even those receiving surgery could not be considered howling successes. Even in a country which takes a very conservative approach to surgery as compared to the United States, the success rate of those returning to work was only one third for any of the surgical groups. The three various techniques had about the same result, except the more complex technique had more complications.

When this paper was first presented at the International Society for the Study of the Lumbar Spine, during the discussion period, I commented to the authors of the paper that it represented a tribute to the docile but stoic attitude of the Swedish patients. They apparently allowed themselves to be randomized to continued, ineffective care. It must have been quite a selling job for the organizers of this study to convince those patients to accept their lot to be randomized to a treatment program which had offered no benefit in pain control and had made the others in the study group candidates for surgical care. The authors responded that they were provided usual care. That's the state of the art of nonoperative care in the civilized world, however. It underlines the need for a better approach.

Who Supplies the Care?

In the free capitalistic society of the United States and many other Western countries, entrepreneurs flourish in all industries. In a basic industry such as electrical power supply and other utilities, there is significant regulation. There is, indeed, regulation in medicine in terms of the qualifications of many practitioners. Certainly health care, as provided by medical and osteopathic doctors, has significant licensing requirements which, to a certain extent, have been nationalized. Initially, states varied as to their requirements and tests required before license was awarded but, still on state-by-state control, the requirements are standardized. Certain basic requirements in education and experience are required before any individual can sit for the proficiency tests. Now most entities require updated testing every ten years or so. To a lesser extent, this is true in the licensing of physiotherapists and chiropractors. Indeed, in California, chiropractors are defined as physicians as they deal with the injured worker. They cannot provide prescription medications but can certainly provide an array of nonoperative care and rehabilitation, as can the physical therapist. (In the rest of the world, those carrying out this craft are called physiotherapists.)

There are also licensing requirements for physical therapy assistants in the United States. Credentialing for those working in exercise science is achieved by graduation from appropriate educational programs. In the case of athletic trainers and some exercise physiologists, the specialty requires certification. Other classifications in the field of exercise science are kinesiologists, who have a higher representation of graduates in other countries, such as Canada, New Zealand and Australia, than in the United States. Their society also requires certification. No governmental licensing, however, is required for the exercise science people. To a certain extent, this is because, at present, they cannot be reimbursed directly from various types of insurance such as workers' compensation, private insurance and Medicare/Medicaid. Thus, they usually work in organizations as salaried employees, supervised by either physiotherapists or physicians. They also work as personal trainers. Thus the quality of care provided by exercise science professionals is not regulated as highly as physicians.

Occupational therapists, whose education is of similar duration and quality as physical therapists, do require state certification but cannot bill independently. Occupational therapy, as contrasted with physical therapy, is more focused at upper extremity function often after hand and arm surgery, reconstruction and vocational evaluation. In some settings, there is a minor turf battle between the orbits of influence of OT versus PT.

As referred to earlier, another group provides nonoperative care. These are the personal trainers. Often they can achieve a type of certification, merely taking weekend courses or courses lasting several weeks. These courses are focused on the principles of exercise with some review of the necessary physiology. They tend to be private entrepreneurs or work in health clubs. Lacking any consistent licensing organization for the wide array of varied training programs, the quality and skill of these individuals can vary widely. They often do not use exercise machines. Customized care can best be sold by manual resistance exercises. Reimbursement by insurance is seldom available.

Add to this mix of providers, the various providers of complementary care such as massage therapists, homeopaths, acupuncturists and chiropractors. Each has certification arrangements within their societies. Reimbursement of these clinicians by various insurance policies varies according to different insurance plans. They are classed under the umbrella of "complementary care". In that they provide, certainly, largely very safe care, often hands-on care and often warm human contact, they are becoming progressively more sought after by the public at large.

However, with none of these therapy providers is there a mechanism for quality control. No documentation of efficacy in treatment is necessary to achieve reimbursement. Of course, if the treatment is being offered outside of the medical reimbursement system, continued care by one of these providers is on the basis of patient perception of efficacy. Often this is enhanced by the charismatic enthusiasm of the provider.

In my experience, it is not unusual to find a patient with a chronic musculoskeletal problem such as neck pain or back pain, who has had chiropractic care or massage therapy for perhaps years. When asked if they are getting better, they say "no". When asked why they continue to receive treatment from their chosen provider, they consistently say they feel better after the treatment. To put their statements in context, I often comment that many of us feel better after two martinis as well, but that certainly does not mean it is a benefit for the particular problem being treated. The project is to get better, not just feel better briefly.

The point of this discussion is that there is a wide variety of providers of nonoperative care with varied degrees of certification and licensing. The only thing consistent about them is that there is no quality control associated with their care based on measurement of results. One might level the same criticism at the medical profession and, in many cases, it is justified. Nonetheless, hospital committees, medical societies and medical malpractice are powerful agents to maintain an accepted standard of care. That, indeed, may be an error as will be discussed later. Nonetheless, the standard of care for medicine and surgery is rather consistent across the nation and, indeed, across the Western civilized world. Those powerful forces mentioned above, however, do not pertain to nonoperative care for musculoskeletal problems.

Where Does the Money Go?

As mentioned at the beginning of this chapter, there are significant factors which are core issues in our discussion—pain control and credibility. We have discussed many of the providers of therapy, whose main purpose is pain control, hopefully associated with correction of the underlying physical problem. The credibility of this care is variable and, as pointed out, the care is seldom measured. A significant factor in credibility, as always in life, is where are the financial benefits. This is where the concept of a medical-industrial complex becomes pertinent. Who is making money from the provision of care? Often the big financial beneficiaries are not clearly visible to the public. Certainly the public recognizes that physicians make a living—often a very good living—from providing care. This is especially true of surgeons. What is not so clearly visible are the powerful financial forces focused on providing surgeons and hospitals with more and more technically advanced equipment.

Many times it is the manufacturers who are pushing increasing utilization of more unproven equipment or designs which are quite redundant to already existing designs. There are over 150 different designs for a total hip. That's because many manufacturers are competing for market share. With total hips, it is the same question as to which is better, a Ford or a Chevrolet? It depends upon what the criterion for better is.

When it comes to treatment of musculoskeletal disease, the same realities exist. There are many different designs for the screws, plates, rods, clamps used in lumbar fusion, for instance. Yet none have been proven to be consistently superior to others. Each of these instruments is supplied at a price far in excess of the pure manufacturing process and raw materials. As long as insurance covers the cost of the implants, the sky is the limit. There are very few ways of controlling these charges in that the hospital which purchases the devices passes the cost to the medical insurance. The medical insurance company raises the rates. The consumer really has no way of understanding why the rates are raised. There are so many factors.

Worse than that, manufacturers push devices and concepts with glowing advertising and company supported research long before their benefit has been proven. A perfect example of this phenomenon is the recent development of what is called the IDET procedure. That stands for intradiscal electrothermal therapy. This is a wire filament which is passed into the intervertebral disc and heats the tissue, allegedly to shrink the tears associated with disc degeneration. The FDA approved this concept without any evidence of its efficacy. No one has seen the disc tears of degeneration change after the procedure. No one knows really how it works. Worse than that, although the manufacturer supported research that documented a high level of success in patients treated, as time has passed, it turns out that this simple treatment, which essentially cooks the inside of the intervertebral disc, is successful in only a third of the patients, of no benefit in another third and another third are worse. Recent studies have shown it is no better than a placebo. Yet this is still being pushed by the manufacturer because of the high profitability of selling this piece of wire for many hundreds of dollars. Almost co-conspirators in this saga are the insurance companies, which are aware of the poor success rate but, again, merely pass the cost on to the public. No one has ever gone back to heavy work following an IDET procedure. All of the same workers' compensation agencies are aware of this but, out of fear of litigation, they do not publish it.

We in the spine world are about to see a new spasm of costs in the form of total disc replacements. Certainly this is a step forward in the care of the painful back for some patients but the utilization of this procedure is being carried out without much long-term experience. There are already five different designs under investigation and, no doubt, there will be many more as the example of the total hip demonstrates.

As you see, credibility has little to do with the equipment supplied to hospitals and surgeons. How much money there is to be made is a major factor. This is no doubt a cynical view. It is true, however, certainly in spine care, that many of the operations that are carried out for pain are unnecessary in that the problems could be corrected by appropriate nonoperative care. We will discuss this from many angles as this story unfolds.

There is yet a more powerful confounding force in the medical industrial complex. A major force here is the pharmaceutical industry. Daily we see advertisements regarding the benefits of various drugs which will stop our pain and improve function. They consistently depict happy, smiling people, carrying out normal functional activities even though they appear to be aged. The success of their function is depicted as related to the intake of some anti-inflammatory or pain-control drug. The implication, of course, is that, with these pharmaceuticals, your problems will be resolved. Only the effort of swallowing a pill is necessary to correct the deficiency of age or injury.

The fact that the advertisements instruct individuals to consult their physicians for treatment with the drug being advertised supplies the cloak of credibility. We should recognize, however, that any pharmaceutical that is being advertised widely in the printed press or on television and radio has a huge marketing budget. The budget for marketing by the various pharmaceutical companies providing these drugs far exceeds the budget for research. That budget includes benefits to doctors who prescribe the medication. The argument that the high prices of drugs, especially in the United States, are necessary to pay for research is quite misleading. All doctors receive a multitude of free drugs. The drug companies hope that they will provide the drugs to their patients as starter doses to allow the patient to become enthusiastic about the proposed benefits. Often, the retail cost of these drugs provided "free" may be up to $100 if received by prescription. The representatives of the pharmaceutical industry are called "detail" men or women. The physician receiving the free drugs is expected to sign a document indicating the receipt of these drugs. The prescription history of each physician is carefully monitored by the pharmaceutical detail people. Rewards are often supplied to the physicians in terms of gifts, dinners, travel, etc., for continued use of a specific drug. Thus, continued use of various agents is very much encouraged by the entrepreneurial organization. In many instances, the benefit of the advertised drug is little different from older, cheaper drugs, which have now become generic. That means that the patents protecting the sale of these drugs have now lapsed and they can be manufactured by any chemical company and thus sold at far lower prices. A constant array of new and "better" drugs is guaranteed by this arrangement. Very few of the new drugs supplied yearly, however, are truly different, new and better.

Here, again, the force of the entrepreneurial spirit suggests that the only responsibility of an individual who has musculoskeletal pain is to see his or her doctor and ask for a prescription. As noted above, the pressure for the doctor to go ahead and prescribe is powerful. To make an argument that other, cheaper drugs would be just as good is inconvenient. It takes time to discourage beliefs which have been generated by powerful advertising. Many doctors don't wish to spend that time and acquiesce without question.

Why Not Therapeutic Exercise?

Yet, all scientific studies that identify the mechanism which offers the opportunity for an individual to "get better" rather than just feel better for a while indicate that active progressive exercise is that way. The physiology is quite simple. Living tissue improves with use, but deteriorates with disuse. Bones become osteoporotic absent physical stresses. Muscles atrophy when placed at rest. Before our current capacity to fix fractures with all manner of internal fixation to allow early function, plaster casts which were applied to treat fractures had to be changed at monthly intervals because they became loose due to the atrophy of the unused muscles in the casted extremity. The cast became loose and started to rub various prominences, offering no external support for the fracture being treated. The importance of use even applies to connective tissue such as ligaments and tendons. They, too, without the stimulation of function, slowly become weaker lacking stimulus for these tissues to build new collagen. In all living tissues, there is a constant turnover of material. The rate varies somewhat, based on the blood supply and function of the tissue. Nonetheless, in spite of low turnover of connective tissue in tendons and ligaments absent the stimulus of stress of normal function, the collagen which makes up the tissue will not be rebuilt when old collagen is removed. Collagen is essentially leather, which has been treated to remove the other material in our living structures. It can withstand significant tension when trained but, absent the mechanical stresses, it will tear from its origins or tear in midportion.

The phenomenon described above is accepted by all involved with the physiology of living organisms. All medical providers would agree with the accuracy of those comments. In our society today, however, mechanisms to achieve the benefits of active progressive exercise are seldom adequately explained.

As an example, recently, the New Zealand government recognized the gradual deterioration of the population due to degenerative changes, obesity and inactivity. They therefore authorized what is called a "green prescription", which is an endorsement by the physician for the patient to proceed into an exercise program. No further directions are supplied. What is missing is a mechanism to locate or reimburse an exercise program or a monitoring of the skill or education of those providing the care. Although public funds support the medical care, they do not support the exercise care.

No such prescription exists in the United States. Physicians seldom supply details for active care. Although, as noted above, they certainly would not deny its benefits, it just takes too long to be specific or to provide endorsement to specific practitioners. Most physicians have had no training in therapeutic exercise.

The story I'm about to tell describes my education in this area. I, too, was once one of those physicians who paid lip service to active exercise but did not have a basic understanding of how, where and who should provide it. My understanding of the possibilities of exercise, however, has now converted me from an enthusiastic, perhaps single-minded, surgeon to a physician with a broader view. I am still respectful of the place of appropriate surgery but I am concerned that far too much surgery and other ineffective medical care is being provided to our population. Many of the problems could be avoided with proper exercise. As I describe my journey of discovery, the story of how we got there and how far we have to go will unfold.

2

Off to a Good Start

I had the great good luck to be born in the depths of the Depression. Certainly, life was not lucky for most people at that time, but I was born on the good side of want to a doctor's family. My father was, indeed, an orthopedic surgeon, whose practice had just begun to develop. I was lucky also because of the values of thrift and "waste not, want not" attitude instilled in us as children of the Depression.

Life had been quite a struggle for him and, thus, he provided a format of values which would serve me throughout the rest of my career. His history provides some nice insight into some positive aspects of American society. It is worth telling because it reinforces the happy opportunities available to us in this free land. As my story unfolds, I may become somewhat cynical but it is certainly not a reaction to the events of life when I recall my father's problems.

It turns out that he was the youngest of eight children in a German-Irish family in the city of Allegheny. In 1901, it became part of Pittsburgh, Pennsylvania, the growing city across the Allegheny River just south of the smaller community of Allegheny. His father was a railroad engineer and thus they lived in a very blue-collar neighborhood. Unfortunately, when my father was three, his father was killed in a railroad accident.

Actually, such incidents were not that rare in those years before many safety regulations were in place. Explosions and derailings were common in the railroad world. The event did leave his poor wife a widow with eight growing children to bring up. Their poverty became more severe. In those days, a social safety net was nonexistent.

Problems for Voigt

Worse than that, when my father was ten, he developed an ailment not uncommon in the depressed neighborhoods of cities. Dad's name was Voigt. He was named after the general practitioner who had delivered him. It was a fairly common German surname. Voigt developed tuberculosis of his hips.

Medical care at that time was scarce, spotty and extremely limited, especially to families with minimal resources. The older kids in the family were working to help support the rest, but certainly there were not enough funds to support significant medical care. Fortunately, their housing was a not-too-distant streetcar ride from a major hospital —the Allegheny General Hospital—which had considerable financial support for free clinics from the wealthy steel and coal entrepreneurs who lived in Allegheny. At that time, it was a pleasant suburb of Pittsburgh. The beautiful Victorian homes of these wealthy executives were nicely placed in the rolling hills of Allegheny—reasonably distant from the belching steel mills which gave Pittsburgh its purpose.

Pittsburgh at that time was a total industrial city with many varied ethnic groups slowly climbing the long ladder of financial and social achievement. That was the promise that brought these immigrants to the city. Most were first generation, only a few yet in the second generation. There were Greeks, Slavs, Italians, Russians—all with varied religions and cuisines. At that time, there were few Blacks or

Hispanics. The Scotch, Irish and Germans had come there a generation earlier. Most worked in steel mills, the coal mines, the glassworks and the ever-continuing construction. It was a true melting pot.

But back to Voigt's problem—what to do about his painful hips. Indeed, at the free clinic in the Allegheny General Hospital, there was an orthopaedic surgeon. That was Dr. David Silver, the first orthopaedic surgeon in the area. That, indeed, seems to be an appropriate name for a doctor who supplied the help needed at this time with the dark cloud of disease.

It was customary at that time for the well-funded hospitals to have free clinics because these were the training grounds for the young physicians who had recently graduated from medical school. The trainees in more specialized areas were called residents because they lived in the hospital to care for the patients of the doctors who had a private practice. None of the residents or the interns, who also worked in the hospitals the first year after medical school, received any salary. They received room and board and uniforms—that's all. They sustained their existence by various moonlighting jobs, which were not restrained by the hospital as long as they carried out the assigned duties.

Dr. Silver evaluated Voigt and carried out the treatment of the day for his problem. He was placed in a large plaster cast to allow the hips to freeze in a usable position. So, from about the age of twelve, Voigt no longer had any motion in his hips, but could stand independently and walk with a somewhat waddling gait. The lost hip range of motion was picked up by greater-than-normal lumbar spine range of motion. Such a treatment, known as auto-fusion, works best in a growing individual so that the greater stresses on the lumbar spine can be absorbed with continued growing tissue adjustment. If such an event happens in an elderly person, i.e.

bilateral hip fusion, it is unlikely that they would be able to walk without considerable assistance.

Nonetheless, because of his disability, many vocations were no longer available to Voigt. Thankfully, with the cooperation of his siblings, it was agreed that he should proceed through life with the use of his head and hands rather than any sort of demanding physical undertaking. Thus, he was one of two graduates of his high school class who went on to college.

He did go on to the University of Pittsburgh and later to the medical school. Following internship, he started a general practice in a suburb of what was now the North Side of Pittsburgh. As the years went by, the practice gradually prospered. Because his practice prospered, and because of his obvious interest in bone and joint disease via his own problems, he became a resident in Orthopaedic Surgery under the very doctor who had cared for him in Allegheny General Hospital. It's a wonderful American story. The benefits of free care provided the vehicle for this poor kid with enough talent and energy to become a successful medical specialist.

A more important aspect of his personal life, however, was an infatuation with a pretty young nurse at Allegheny General Hospital, where he worked. Naomi Solomon came from a German Lutheran farm family in central Pennsylvania. Few opportunities were available for women in the early 1920s, other than teaching and nursing. To Naomi, a nursing career seemed a happy choice to escape the drudgery of farm work. Much to the consternation of her mother and father, she took the train to the big city hospital 200 miles away to begin her career as a nurse. After finishing nursing training, she took over a crippled children's facility in Sewickley, Pennsylvania. Shortly thereafter, Voigt and Naomi were married by the Presbyterian minister at the First Presbyterian Church in Pittsburgh. Thus, the family had begun.

In 1931, therefore, my adventure began. I was the second child of four. There was an older brother and two younger sisters. By the time I was three, my father had collected enough financing to build a wonderful stone house on the highest hill in Pittsburgh zoned for housing. It was only fifteen feet lower than the municipal reservoir, which was, indeed, on the highest hill in the city. I remember the plaque at the top of the steps, which proudly stated, 1332 FEET ABOVE SEA LEVEL. We could see for miles from this vantage point.

Adventures in Growing Up

It was a wonderful place to grow up. At that time, it was flanked on all sides by what we children called "the woods". This was undeveloped land which had been forested many years earlier but there were new growth trees, forty to fifty years old, and it was highly thicketed. Rabbits and even deer roamed in the area which, at that time, was about half an hour by trolley ride from center city. Later, with the highways that were put in, it was fifteen minutes from the city. From the house, there was a hearty mile walk, mostly downhill, into the little shopping area known as "Perry View". The road at the bottom of the hill was at that time called Perry Highway, which became Perrysville Avenue as it crossed the city limits at the base of the hill on which the house was built. This house situated at the crest of the hill was named by my mother "Four Winds" and the road leading down to the highway was called Four Winds Road. This was, for many years, an unpaved gravel road but it did supply a wonderful road for sledding and a devil of a road for the car to climb when there was snow. On some occasions, cars became stuck and could not make the final 500–600 feet due to the severity of the incline and one had to walk up to the house on top of the hill. Those problems didn't seem to bother us kids at the time.

At the beginning of this story, I said I was "lucky" enough to be born in the middle of the Depression. This was not a happy event for most of the population but there were lessons for the children. Our parents, as typical of everyone at that time, were extremely frugal. Nothing was wasted. Plates were always emptied. Thrift and good fiscal habits were encouraged. Along that line, it was decided as we boys grew older that my older brother, Voigt, would be in charge of the gardening. He, of course, was assisted by my mother. He was encouraged to negotiate prices of the produce of the garden for retail to my mother. He would look the prices up in the newspaper and offer a comparable price to my mother, who would negotiate down, offering the arguments of the assistance supplied by the parents in terms of seeds, guidance and free rent. Nonetheless, this was a reasonable source of spending money for movies.

I was placed in charge of growing chickens. A chicken coop had been built next to the dog run. Dad had a real thing for Great Danes and, for many years, we raised several generations of Great Danes who had an extensive run at the back of the property, which was encased in a cyclone fence six feet high to withstand their vigorous jumps. The chicken coop being built beside this run was a source of great pleasure to the dogs, who never tired of harassing the chickens. The chickens, on the other hand, grew quite accustomed to the presence of the dogs and seemed to pay no heed to them. At least, the chickens in charge of laying eggs did so nicely.

It was my job to collect the eggs, feed the chickens and, being instructed to take the good with the bad, to clean out the chicken manure. All was not lost with that little job in that I was encouraged to negotiate a price for fertilizer sale to my brother, in charge of the garden. This was often a hard bargain because he readily recognized that there were no alternative sales for chicken fertilizer. Sometimes we settled for a price of Sen-Sen. Sen-Sen were tiny, licorice squares, measuring less than one-fourth inch across, which one would suck and chew to freshen the breath. A packet would perhaps contain 100 and could be purchased for under five cents. Given the meager value of these things, often the price of fertilizer was negotiated at one Sen-Sen per shovelful. This certainly was good instruction in negotiating from strength or weakness. As could be expected, there were frequent altercations between my brother and me. We seemed to disagree on everything and took great pleasure in pummeling each other, which is not unusual behavior for preteen guys with what seemed then to be inexhaustible energy.

Exploring the woods, occasionally getting lost and talking to one of the Great Danes for hours at a time, softened the blow of having no neighbors. The dogs seemed to understand the "conversations" about my problems. They made no rebuttal.

There was a Catholic convent next door but the nuns could hardly be considered worthy neighbors to a growing boy. Indeed, we had to walk through the convent property to get to the road which led to school, about a mile and a half away. As a preteen, I was often embarrassed while walking down the road that led up to the convent, in that, it was also a private girls' school and the girls walking up the hill, all in their uniforms, would often make fun of me, walking down the hill and going to school, carrying a lunch box, etc. That, perhaps, made me nervous about girls for many years.

It was also often a problem at school that we were lacking any communication with neighbors. Actually, school was in a very blue-collar neighborhood although in a quiet suburban setting. All of the houses were individually built. There were no tract housing operations at that time. The parents worked at varied jobs available to tradesman and non-college graduates.

Nonetheless, because the school was not very large and each class contained six to eight boys, there was always a need for an extra guy to fit into a team if it were to be constructed of roughly the same age group. At that time, thankfully, there were no organized systems of play, such as Little League, soccer or Pop Warner football. There was a rough playground, which had no grass but the dirt was relatively smooth and supplied an appropriate ball field. In the spring, we played "roundsies" until sufficient numbers of players could be collected to have two opposing teams. It was a great lesson in organizational needs if not organizational psychology. We all learned to adjust the rules of the game depending on the number of kids available and their relative skills. Rule adjustments seemed to be easily achieved by consensus when various options had been explored. Sometimes we would play softball, using only two bases rather than three. Perhaps we would give up a shortstop, recognizing that the majority of the team were not good hitters and thus the left fielder probably could handle most balls. Although not apparent then, certainly it became clear in retrospect that one advantage of unorganized sports is that the need to get on with it exceeded the necessity to adhere to prearranged rules. One could adjust the rules and all would accept by consensus. If someone moaned about inappropriate rules after he had made an infraction of the new rules but not the old rules, he was shouted down by the rest. End of argument. Democracy at work. What a pity kids don't have as much opportunity to make up the rules of *their* games. There is a lot of freedom with non-adult sports. It's a marvelous possibility for growth.

The Privileged Education Begins

Because of the limited resources of the local public high school, it was decided that my brother and I should be sent off to private school. It is ironic that my father's terrible tragedy of bilateral frozen hips, forcing him to become educated, allowed him to have the affluence to provide for our excellent education. My brother and I were sent off for the last four years of secondary school to Shady Side Academy. This at the time was both boarding and day school. Some of the kids lived close enough to be brought there by buses, but we lived about twenty miles away. At that time, no family had two cars—my mother didn't even drive. Thus, Voigt and I became five-day boarders and came home on weekends. At that time, it was an all-boys school with fifty to sixty in a class. The teachers were called "masters". The grade levels were called "forms", along the lines of the English public school system (i.e., private schools). Everybody participated in athletics. Everybody had a fairly proscribed teaching program with little alternative for electives. As typical of most, I had four years of Latin, four years of math, four years of history and English. An elective in languages was offered and, because at the time I felt I wanted to go into medicine and most of it in the twentieth century seemed to be coming from Germany, I took German. Given the ebb and flow of historical events, I certainly wish I had taken Spanish.

The value of this teaching system, of course, were the small classes and individual attention. For four years, I had to write what were called "themes", which varied in complexity and length, depending upon the stage of learning. These always were assigned topics and one was expected to construct an article along lines provided by the teacher. This may have been a critique of some book or play, but it may have been a request to write a perspective on some issue of the time, either historical, physical or moral. The value, of course, was a thorough read by the master, who would correct spelling, grammar, paragraph structure, syntax, etc., with red and blue pens and a big grade at the top, circled. Such constant correction made writing easy in later years. I'm afraid it didn't do much for my spelling. I never seemed to get the hang of it.

We competed in sports with other schools in the area. Some were public, and we were also in a league of other private schools, which actually extended from Buffalo to Detroit. Because of our small number of students, it was difficult to assemble skilled teams. In my senior year, we lost every football game. I remember our coach, a previous football star at Pitt, who had become a dentist and worked with us part-time in the autumn afternoons, clarifying the value of the season to us. He said, "Boys, we built a lot of character this year."

Wrestling was another thing, however. Individual skills could emerge. We had a master who was also a science teacher, who had wrestled in college and was knowledgeable. Thus, the wrestling team, on which I competed in the heavyweight division, often did fairly well. Later, in college, thinking I had some talent in that area, I went on to have a casual wrestling match with a young guy who seemed to be a lot smaller, but he challenged me. At that time, I weighed about 180 pounds. He weighed 140. He beat me badly. Later he mentioned that he was state champion from Indiana. My collegiate wrestling career ended right then.

A similar fate ended my football career. Although I played tackle on the line at Shady Side—being one of the bigger guys in our class, I found that the average weight of the linemen in college was way over 200 pounds. I scrimmaged on the freshman team but was frequently mashed and never got above third string. Again, the athletic career happily ended then. Even so, college athletics took a lot of time, were often associated with injuries and were certainly a source of distraction if one's intellectual talents were underwhelming. Some very talented guys could excel in both athletics and academics—but not I.

Thus, I had the great good luck to show up in a relatively affluent family. I had the opportunity to grow. I was nurtured by firm but loving parents. My father was always distant. He demanded great respect and our responses to his questions were expected to be either "yes, sir" or "no, sir". These rules of strictness were meant to mold our characters. Our parents' concern about our character was ever present and represented by the clock that hung above the door in our bedroom. It had a twelve-inch face. It was an electric clock. Dad had emblazoned in a triangle at the 12:00, 4:00 and 7:00 positions on the face, three "C's". These were expected to constantly remind us of the guiding principle of a successful life—Courtesy, Courage and Cooperation. It's amazing how easily I can remember those words.

Although at first I was quite homesick during the five-day boarding, I rather soon got used to it. After all, my brother, three years ahead of me, also was at the same school and gradually I developed my own set of friends. The athletics as well as the extracurricular activities filled the days, and the weekend was associated with chores at home and writing the dreaded theme which had to be done over every weekend.

Gradually, I began to take refuge in church activities in the form of the Young People's Society, where there was an array of girls with various strengths and weaknesses from my tilted adolescent view. One, however, was particularly attractive in that she seemed unusually sensible and self-contained—always self-assured. Ruth and I began to be a couple at various events, starting at age fourteen. We got along well, and also had our puppy love spats as of an on-and-off romance. She began to write to me at school. Her father had died very early in her life, at age four, and she was brought up by her widowed mother, who worked at Gimbel's as a lady's dress buyer. She was a sensible girl. That was demonstrated at school functions. Social events at the prep school often included girls from the two female private schools in Pittsburgh. These, like Shady Side, were same sex entities to which mostly affluent families sent the young ladies. Compared to Ruth, however, I found most of these girls quite air-headed and interested in things which didn't make much sense. Thus, at social events such as proms and parties, Ruth was my general date. She, on the other hand, found she was a bit ostracized in that, lacking any connection with the private school girls, quite typical of that age group, she was ignored and placed outside of their circle of conversation.

Meanwhile, my father, noting the growing interest in Ruth on my part was concerned that it might become truly serious. He, indeed, had not married until he was thirty-four and was quite sure that that was the most appropriate time for a young man to be focused in that direction. Thus, he laid down the law that I could never see Ruth in the form of a date. As things turned out, that certainly taught me a lesson. Don't tell a kid he picked the wrong girl. Such a rule only enhanced my enthusiasm to continue the relationship as it certainly did Ruth's as well. She cried when I told her of the impending restrictions, and it became quite a romantic event. We continued to have secret meetings and concealed dates. Many of the events at church were group affairs anyhow and we could continue to see each other without restraint.

Early Gaps in Medical Care

During this growing period, I had my first encounter with rehabilitation principles—or lack of them. About the age of fifteen, I twisted my knee while playing touch football after I stepped into a hole. My knee quickly became swollen and I could no longer continue playing. I limped around a bit and it got better. Finally, several weeks later, my father noticed the limping and investigating further—extracting the history of injury, etc. After a while, it became clear that I had torn my meniscus and would require surgery. This was duly accomplished and I was placed in a long leg cast (toes to groin) after surgery and continued to use it for six weeks, walking on crutches. Following that, the cast was removed and I was told to tighten my muscles but given no further instructions. It took me months to get the knee back in shape. That was the standard of care at that time, however. I will provide a discussion later as to the events which changed postoperative care. I was in no position to criticize, of course, as this is how one was treated at that time.

Actually, I had quite a bit of exposure to injury. Apparently I was a fairly energetic but perhaps stupid kid as I grew up. I fell on many occasions and broke my right arm on four different occasions. Fortunately, the care was quite inexpensive in that my father, being an orthopaedic surgeon, would come home after being told by mother about my crooked arm. He would snap it straight and place a plaster cast in the correct position. I certainly remember the sting of those reductions which should have been sufficient warning to not injure myself again, but kids have short memories, poor judgement and a lot of energy.

There was another event which was instructive as to my later view of orthopedic care. About the age of twelve, while running after or from somebody at school—I can't remember which way it was—I slipped on a steep hill and hit my back. It hurt quite a bit but I was able to shake it off and continue activity. I found, however, I wasn't any good in sports and I had a backache most of the time. Again, after a week or so, my father noticed my unusual posture and had it X-rayed. It turned out that I had a compression fracture at the lowest thoracic vertebra (T12).

The treatment of the day was to try to correct the height of the compressed fracture. This was done by suspending the individual by the legs while propping the upper chest on a support while the individual was lying face down. In that the compression fracture is always in the front part of the bone, this maneuver, called "hyperextension", was an attempt to correct the deformity. If the fracture was approached soon after the injury, it could be corrected to a certain degree. Following half an hour or so in that position, a full body cast would be placed on the individual. Unfortunately, that maneuver was not successful with me and therefore I was placed in bed for a week in a hyperextended position in an attempt to correct the fracture. I had to lie on my back with the bed propped up in the middle so that my upper chest and legs were lower than my midback. That was an awful position for a twelve-year-old. I was allowed to get up and go to the bathroom and eat but, most of the rest of the time, I had to lie this way. This was done in the hospital. How strange it would be to place somebody in the hospital now with that treatment.

Eventually, the partial correction was accepted and I was placed in a total body cast which, again, I wore for about six weeks. The only benefit from this cast, which I could wear under loose-fitting clothes, was that, when I got into fights at school, when the other kid hit me in the chest, he was surprised and occasionally injured by striking the rock-hard plaster cast. I was temporarily invincible. Eventually the damn cast was removed and I found myself as weak as spaghetti. I recovered slowly but years later, when X-rays were taken, it was discovered that, as reports in the literature (medical journals) had later described, it didn't work. The closed reduction, although successful initially, had dropped back into its original state and T12 was half as high in the front as it was in the back. The total event had been a useless adventure in minor torture from my standpoint. Again, however, I was unaware of these factors as I accepted the events as fate and, although angry at what was going on, I had no way to escape. But this experience gave me some insight for future care.

There seemed to be no major problems in the events at that time. School was going well. Summers went by nicely. My prospects for the future seemed bright. But then my first significant unguarded moment occurred.

A Bend in the Road

It was during the summer of 1948 that a new set of privileges seemed to emerge. I had passed the driving test and my father now started to let me chauffeur him around to his various appointments during the summer. Actually, I was a little surprised at that privilege. Also, I found that he often called me "my son" rather than Vert. I didn't know until later why he placed me in such a posture of heritage rather than familiarity.

Suddenly one day, while I was home, the word came that my father had suddenly died of a heart attack at the hospital. He was preparing to go to surgery. He was in the doctor's locker room, removing his clothes to put on the scrub suit typical of a surgeon. According to other doctors there, he was whistling to himself and it suddenly stopped when he fell. No one was aware of CPR or other resuscitative maneuvers at the time—and he was dead. Of course, the family was devastated. My mother was tearful for weeks. It turned out, however, that my father was aware of the impending doom in that he had consulted physicians as to his chest pain and shortness of breath and was informed that he had serious cardiac disease. No treatment program was available at that time, other than nitroglycerin to help the chest pain. He had made out a will and actually had set up trust funds for all the children's educations. He had fully prepared the family financially for events to come although he had not informed my mother about it. Recognizing her limited capacity in business, he had set up with the bank a special trust fund which allocated her a monthly allowance. This was a source of considerable acrimony as the future unfolded in that the allowance was not truly sufficient.

Nonetheless, suddenly I recognized that now there was far more responsibility for me to solve my own problems. There certainly would be less financial support in the future in that I was informed that the trust fund had a total of $8,000 for my education and future. Being very impressed by what my father did and how he acted, I had determined to be an orthopedic surgeon when I was twelve and thus recognized long years of medical school and training were ahead of me. Would that be enough money? Although not totally, I was certainly on my own more than ever before.

Mother was able to hold the home together. There were sufficient funds to handle daily events. The house had been paid off. There were two boys to get through college, however. Voigt was already off at Princeton—an expensive place even then. The two girls, five and eight years younger than I, had lessons to resolve and an education to be achieved. The times were very difficult for my mother. She never was an unusually warm person and did not develop many friends in the community. She was very strong-willed and was sure she could handle it herself. She did, indeed, do very, very well.

3

The College and Medical School Years

So, it was off to college after graduation at Shady Side Academy. I was lucky enough to get a Lockhart Scholarship to Princeton. This only paid $600 annually, but it was quite a help since the tuition at Princeton in 1949 unbelievably was $600. Once again, I was benefiting from the benevolence of unseen, unknown predecessors such as those who had established the free clinic at Allegheny General Hospital. Now, by this mechanism, I could gain a marvelous education. When there seems to be so much financial waste in the world, it is difficult to measure the benefit of these small bits and pieces of assistance which provide a value magnified many times over by their benefits. An unexpected event, yes, an unguarded moment had made it possible to gain a major step up toward a successful career.

Although certainly most of the students at Princeton came from affluent families, the university made major efforts to provide help for the underfunded. They had a system organized, known as the Bureau of Student Aid. All concessions at the university were staffed by students with financial needs. There were a lot of part-time jobs, ranging from attendants at the parking lots during the football games to waiters in the dining halls. I stumbled across a marvelous classmate who was a real entrepreneur, Bob Luton, who had been in the Navy prior to getting a scholarship to Princeton. We became roommates. He had grown up under the wing of a widowed Italian-Swiss mother in the weaving industry in Secaucus, New Jersey. He had no potential after finishing high school and thus joined the Navy. In that he spoke Italian, he became the official translator to the Captain of the ship to which he was assigned during a tour of the Mediterranean. The Captain, recognizing his talent, got him involved with a scholarship program that the Navy had organized to recruit officers. In an exchange for his college education, he had four years of Navy service to pay back as an officer after college. With that background, however, he was quite savvy.

Bob became student director of the Bureau of Student Aid. We had a nicely furnished room because he was also in charge of the furniture exchange. In another demonstration of the value of knowing the right people, Bob put me in charge of the beer mug agency. Nearly every student had one to two beer mugs emblazoned with the Princeton emblem and their year of graduation. I had salesmen working for me who were also students but, because I was the guy in charge of orders and procuring the beer mugs, I got a piece of each sale.

Between part-time jobs, summer jobs, the trust fund, the scholarship, I stumbled through those years financially. It was exciting. I don't remember feeling any envy for the students from rich families. I felt extremely lucky to be there.

You Can't Always Plan It Out

Under the heading of the unguarded moment, this is a good time to tell a little story which taught me the value of risk taking and "chutzpah". I met a fellow scholarship student, Carl Lyle, in the course of the Bureau of Student Aid activities. He had arrived at Princeton by a most curious route. It turns out that, as a young high school student in Rogersville, Tennessee, he recognized that none of his teachers had ever received degrees from a higher college than a Tennessee Normal School. Thus, application to universities outside of the Tennessee system would not be credible. He thus felt his potentials were very limited. On the basis of that, he organized a strike of the student body of the high school, who allegedly lay down in the middle of the main road through Rogersville and stopped traffic. This got attention, all right. He was thrown out of school. Nonetheless, some benevolent soul heard the story and recruited him to attend the Hun School in New Jersey. This was a very good prep school. Carl was a pretty small guy—weighing perhaps 130 pounds. Nonetheless, he was wiry and strong. Also, this was the time when the T-formation quarterback had just become the next step forward in football strategy. At that time, the T-formation quarterback just had to hand the ball off to various scampering backfield members or else fade back and pass it himself. Carl did that very well and the Hun School went on to be state champions that year. Of all things, he got an athletic scholarship for his football prowess. That was short-lived. In fact, he became the coxswain on the crew because of his diminutive size.

With that background, he, too, had a lot of street smarts. One day he suggested we should spend a weekend in New York. He had just purchased a 1932 Chevy Coupe for a Glenn Miller phonograph album. That gives you an idea of the expected value of this jalopy. It had a crack in the engine block and could only go twenty to thirty miles before all of the oil came out of the engine. I was therefore surprised when Carl said, "Let's go to New York for the weekend." New York is about fifty miles north of Princeton and, worse than that, I only had about $1.50 in cash. I pointed out those two facts to Carl but that didn't disturb him at all. Thus, Friday afternoon, we cruised toward New York. Every fifteen miles or so, we would stop at a gas station and Carl would play the dumb kid role and ask for any used oil they had. We would dump that in the engine and be off again for the next fifteen to twenty miles. We made it to New York with three gas station stops. At that time, it cost fifty cents to take the Holland Tunnel from New Jersey to the city and thus one third of my funds had already disappeared.

It was early evening and we pulled up at a fire hydrant in front of a well-known Dixieland club in Greenwich Village. Willie "the Lion" Smith was playing the piano that night. Carl had instructed me to take a tennis ball with me before we left. We therefore sat at the bar of the club (you didn't have to pay the cover charge if you sat at the bar) and started to drink our beers. He told me to slow down and I saw why after the set had been completed. The musicians stopped playing for a while and he took the ball out of his pocket and placed it into the glass, thus sealing it off. He slipped the glass, 2/3 filled with beer, into his coat pocket. I did the same and we walked to the next bar. We felt safe about getting a ticket in that the car looked so old and dilapidated and Carl had propped up the hood so that any policeman who wandered by would be quite sure it had died a natural death right there. Likewise, we were a bit past the edge of honesty when we pulled this beer trick several times. A bartender finally noticed and threw us out. We then wandered up to the theater district. All of the theaters have an intermission, wherein the patrons would drift out into the lobby between acts for coffee and drinks. Often, they would even spill outside of the lobby onto the street. We were nicely dressed. We easily mingled with the crowd but held back as they moved in for the next act. Being at the tail end of those going back to their seats, we quickly spotted two empty seats toward the back of the theater and sat down. We saw the last two acts of *Darkness at Noon*.

At the conclusion of the evening's entertainment, I turned to Carl and said, "Well, what now?" He fished ten cents out of his pocket and made a phone call on the nearby pay phone to a friend, a girl he had met at some dance recently. It turned out that she lived on Park Avenue, the parents had left for the weekend and she said the butler would let us in. Thus, the next day was spent sightseeing and eating at her place, keeping her and a girlfriend entertained. Delightful. Sunday morning, we were on our way back. There was another fifty cents that went to the tunnel. Carl had agreed to pay for the gas and thus I was back at the dorm on Sunday afternoon, still with fifty cents in my pocket.

Carl was not great in academics but nonetheless he went to Columbia University Medical School, as did I. However, he was about to lose his scholarship to medical school at the end of the first year. He actually was in the Dean's office for that event when a very successful alumnus called the office and wanted to set up a scholarship for students at the bottom of the class. Carl got it. What a charmed life! He later married the professor's daughter and he, himself, became Professor of Internal Medicine at Duke. I learned a lot from Carl.

I had moved happily through the years at college and had a joyous graduation in June of 1953. A week later, Ruth and I married and, a week later, we moved to New York, where I was about to start medical school at Columbia Physicians and Surgeons. We chose New York City as the place to live for the next four years because Ruth, working for Gulf Oil, could transfer to an office in New York City. She did so and, thankfully, supported me through medical school for the next four years.

Although, of course, medical school is an extended series of unexpected revelations and educational moments, there was nothing unique or career altering, it was all pretty much as expected.

But there was one unexpected interface which was unusually instructive. It taught me that intelligence and talent need not correlate with credibility and respectability. There was a student in our class who had graduated from Yale, who seemed to be one of the smartest guys there. He also was a marvelous artist who could reproduce the various pathology slides we were studying in such expert drawings that he became an assistant to the professor. At the end of our second year, he also was organizing short trips to Europe through a travel agency scheme he had developed. Just about the time the travel arrangement scheme fell apart, however, he was no longer present in class at the beginning of our third year. At that point, there was a series of articles in the newspaper about a cat burglar who attended various socialite parties in Newport and the Hamptons as a guest. Later, he ransacked the houses, having determined the location of the valuables during the course of the evening. They caught the burglar. It was our smart fellow student from Yale. I suppose he finally got out of jail. At medical school, he was so good at what he did, I was sure he would make a good doctor. I guess he just wanted to be good at everything.

After an internship at the University of Pittsburgh Hospital and two years as a Navy doctor at Camp Pendleton, I returned to Pittsburgh and started on my real road of discovery.

A Series of Surprising Characters

There were several events during the medical school years which did provide an insight to how life goes. They are not perhaps relevant to my education as to alternatives to surgery but they do shine a light on necessary aspects of life—the need for varied experiences to educate one about other points of view.

The first episode actually happened between the first and second years of medical school. This was the only occasion during the medical school years when I had time off. Thereafter, medical school assignments took up all twelve months of the year. However, being aware of this upcoming event, Ruth and I answered an ad in *The New York Times* about January of 1950 for a job as a waiter on Nantucket Island. Of course, neither of us had been to Nantucket Island, and the fact that I had never been a waiter really didn't make much difference. We answered the ad and got word that our offer had been accepted. Thus, at the conclusion of the first year of medical school, in mid-June of that year, we traveled to Nantucket Island and the restaurant where we were going to work. It was actually a famous old restaurant and hotel called Wauwinet House. It sits at the far northern tip of Nantucket Island in a remarkable area. On the east side of the property is the Atlantic Ocean with its variable surf. On the west side, about a quarter of a mile distant, was a broad lagoon with very placid waters, quite appropriate for sailing. The water was shallow and easily warmed up during the summer to make swimming very pleasant.

When we arrived at Wauwinet House, we found that all the other "waiters" had answered similar ads and had absolutely no qualifications and absolutely no previous experience. Most were in postgraduate training—in law school, a few in medical school and even a few English and philosophy majors. There were seven of us. There was, indeed, one oddball. This was a very pleasant guy who was already a practicing lawyer in Yugoslavia and was taking graduate courses at Harvard Law School. We, of course, were in our late twenties and he was about thirty-two. His seniority qualified him to be assigned the job as the bartender. Ruth, indeed, being the only female in the crowd, was assigned to be hostess at the hotel restaurant. It was also a new job to her. It required arranging seating for the various guests, organizing special meals and parties, etc. Nonetheless, her position made her senior to the waiters.

Actually, Wauwinet House was a very desolate place. By design, it was a summer resort for people who "wanted to get away from all". Many families had come there for many years to take advantage of the pleasant summer weather, the sailing and surfing, and the total absence of distractions. There was no theater, no television, hardly any radios. We were ten miles from the nearest settlement south of us in Nantucket.

After a while, Bronco, our Yugoslavian bartender (full name Bronco Volcmer), moaned to us that he was disturbed that there were no women around. Actually, the only women on the staff were Ruth and a young lady from Boston who was with the jazz combo that had been employed to play in the evenings for the dancing in the casino at the hotel. She was only eighteen and, surprisingly, she was in charge of playing bass fiddle with the saxophone and drums played by the two other members of the combo. Actually, even to us, she was not very attractive. After about two weeks, Bronco says to us, "Vat is dis place?" There were no women. He said that he would have to take out the guests.

The rest of us were not so sure that was a good idea, this being a family resort and all. We also were curious who he would take out. As far as we could see, all of the women were married with children and, because this was a rather expensive place, most were in the older age group from rather affluent backgrounds in the Midwest of the United States. He reassured us by saying, "I only take out married women over thirty-five." Of course, for the rest of us in our late twenties, we were astonished at those criteria. Upon questioning, he clarified his judgement on the issue. He stated that he liked "experienced" women and he said, in the older age group, "they are so grateful". Actually, none of us could argue with his justification.

He was getting progressively more restless and finally we decided to settle the matter by drawing up a wager. One afternoon, one of the law students made book on the proposed seduction. Given what we perceived to be extremely severe odds—married women over thirty-five there with their husbands and children—we gave him very good odds. We pooled our money and set it aside.

On a specific day, the meter started running and we all hovered around him as he chose the appropriate candidate for the seduction. This turned out to be Mrs. Green from Cincinnati. She had come there for ten years. There were four little Greens in the summer cottages along the beach. She was, of course, there with her husband, a stockbroker from Cincinnati. There she sat at the bar, more or less toying with her drink, when Bronco said, "Vat would you *really* like to drink?"

She looked up and said, "Well, I have a gin and tonic."

Then, he said, "No, no. Vat would you *really* like?" It went on from there, I guess.

Two days later, the desk clerk, also a college student—actually an English major at Harvard—was sitting at breakfast with Ruth. They did this daily to plan for the incoming guests, table allocations, etc. Jerry said, "You can't believe what happened last night in my cabin." It turns out all of the help lived in old, weather-beaten, boarded dressing rooms of an earlier era. There was no insulation in the walls between one room and another. It happened that Bronco had the cabin next to Jerry's. Jerry said, "Bronco had Mrs. Green in his cabin last night."

Of course, Ruth said, "Well, what did they do?"

Jerry said, "I can't tell you."

Of course, Ruth said, "Come on, what did they really do?"

"Oh, it was awful," Jerry said.

Jerry went on to say, "Oh, the things they said. The things they did. I can't tell you what happened."

Ruth got the picture and later, when our paths crossed after the breakfast meal, she said, "Bronco had Mrs. Green in his room last night."

I said, "Oh, damn!"

She said, "What do you mean, 'oh, damn'? So what?"

I really couldn't tell her how much money I had lost on that bet.

There is a lesson that there is never a sure thing.

Bronco went on to have several more romantic adventures that summer until one of the husbands finally got wind of the project and Bronco was fired. He ended up giving historical tours to tourists from the mainland who came in every day by boat. He had the choice of multiple unattached young ladies and he survived quite nicely.

Years later, I had a speaking event at Zagreb, Yugoslavia, and Ruth came along. When I came back from the conference in the late afternoon, I found Ruth leafing through the phone book. I said, "Really, what are you doing?"

She said, "Well, Bronco lived in Zagreb and I'm trying to find his number. Now, I've made the cut." Indeed, she was over thirty-five and married!

There's yet another story on a totally different level, which describes how customs and accepted medical practice have changed.

In the third year of medical school, we at Columbia Presbyterian Hospital had a rotation at the Bellevue Hospital in downtown Manhattan. This famous old municipal hospital had already served 100 years. It had huge, cavernous wards which had fifty patients to a ward. There was a side ward which the medical students labeled "the flight deck" in that patients who were seriously ill transferred to this ten-bedside ward. Very few ever returned to the regular ward. Doctors had so little skills in intensive care and so little skills in caring for emergencies that those who were near death usually achieved that goal without much help from the medical profession.

The place was very understaffed and mostly staffed by very tired medical residents. I remember an episode where we three eager young medical students who were serving as what was called "clinical clerks" were being instructed by the resident in charge of a huge ward. He had been up all night and was obviously very tired and harried. He was smoking a cigarette which, unbelievably, then was quite customary. After he finished his smoke, he dropped it on the floor and squeezed it out. He noted the concern from the medical students and said, "Oh, yeah. For goodness' sake, never pick anything up from the floor. It's really dirty here." Somehow he didn't see that it was his fault that the place was dirty. Somehow he didn't see the terrible scourge tobacco had laid upon otherwise intelligent people.

There is just one more story under the auspices of the unguarded moment, which presents an instructive event to me.

As all medical students at the time, I was signed up to serve in the military service at some time during or after medical school. This was in the late 1950s. Following completion of my internship in mid-1958, I was signed up to join the Navy. One of the residents with whom I had worked in internship had told me about a special deal called "photo-fluorography" that the Navy had. In this arrangement, the job was to read many chest X-rays to try to detect any chest disease—especially tuberculosis, in the Navy and Marine recruits. I was trained to do this and I read perhaps two million chest films during the course of my career as a navy photofluorographist. This did not take a full day but I could not serve as a general medical officer when I was assigned to Camp Pendleton. Thus, in typical Navy fashion, whenever there was an opening due to the doctor being transferred or on short term leave, I was plugged into these positions. It made no difference that I had only just finished my internship.

It turned out that, on one occasion, the base psychiatrist was sent off to take a special training course. I was assigned the role of base psychiatrist. This was different than the hospital psychiatrist, which is really a professional, and my role was to serve only the troops at Camp Pendleton Marine Base.

A few weeks after I took this position, one of the company commanders sent a young man for psychiatric evaluation and treatment. It turns out his problem was stuttering. Stuttering is extremely hard to correct. There are psychological as well as physical reasons for this problem.

While at college at Princeton, my roommates and I had checked out a book from the library by Dr. Mesmer. He had described ways of "hypnotizing" people. That was his phrase. We gain the word "mesmerized" from that technique. The essence of the system was to gain an individual's complete attention and then slowly instruct them to carry out various maneuvers. We roommates had grown proficient at this and became able to hypnotize each other so that we could make an arm get cold and another arm get warm. I remember specifically one occasion when I had given my roommate a posthypnotic suggestion that he would be asleep at midnight. Indeed, he was playing cards in a class-mate's room and, at midnight, I said, "Bob, what time is it?" He looked at his watch and fell asleep. We carried him down to our room, dropping him once. He stayed asleep. Then I became aware that I had not told him when to wake up. I watched him over the rest of the night, fearful that he would never awaken. Thank goodness, at the usual time, 6:30 in the morning, he awakened and seemed to have no problems. Our insight into hypnotism was not very deep.

Nonetheless, that was the only semi-psychiatric maneuver of which I was aware. Therefore, I decided to hypnotize this young guy, who actually had grown up in Pittsburgh, my hometown. This was the era where Bing Crosby was a crooner and in many of the movies he was seen to be smoking a pipe. He appeared to be quite "cool" in his performance. Therefore, I gave him a posthypnotic suggestion to be a pipe smoker. Indeed, he did so and actually seemed more relaxed and actually stopped his stuttering. I was as surprised as he was.

Several weeks later, the same company commander sent another Marine over to correct his imbalance. In this case, the young man wet the bed at night. That's even more difficult to treat in an adult. Again, it is a psychological problem and actually not a urologic problem in that setting. I made him a pipe smoker also for totally unjustifiable reasons.

In a couple of weeks, the real psychiatrist showed up and looked at my records. His summation was: "Mooney, what is this shit?"

Indeed, only two of the fifty patients I had seen were effectively treated with hypnotism. With the rest, I tried various drugs and some worked and some didn't.

As a result of that interface, I was assigned to be the physician to the brig.

That was interesting also. The Marines are a bit weird about inmates in the brig seeking medical attention. Any of those who wished to see the doctor while serving in the brig were marched up to the dispensary, about a quarter of a mile away from the brig, for my evaluation. Each Marine was asked to carry a daisy and lay it on the doctor's desk before they were evaluated. The Marines have a hard time with what they define as a "candy ass".

The psychiatric interlude, from my standpoint, did have a benefit. Later on, I was assigned to another clinic. This was a new event. Up to that time, females had only served in the Marines in secretarial-type jobs. These were actually in Marine Corps training positions. These female Marines were assigned to a specific compound surrounded by barbed wire, ten miles into the desert. The Marines identified these young ladies as "BAMS" (broad-ass Marines). I was in charge of sick call.

Each day perhaps ten percent of the contingent would show up with all sorts of complaints of unusual pains which sometimes ranged into the ridiculousness of pains in their fingernails and toenails. Of course, the basic problem was that they had no social contact. They were fenced in in this desert location.

One day, one young lady showed up and she has a totally different problem. She was, by golly, pregnant. How that happened with all the barbed wire I have no idea.

Nonetheless, when I reported the problem to the medical service corps officer (the guy in charge of administration of the unit), he said, "Well, survey her out." I pointed out to him, on the various documents used for the process of discharging Marines for medical reasons, that there was no spot for pregnancy. The Marine Corps had never before experienced pregnancy as a justification for discharge.

On the other hand, I was familiar with the code numbers for psychiatric illnesses and we signed her out as hysterical. Actually, that is somewhat scientifically relevant in that it was initially thought that the abnormal ideas of females were secondary to hormones emerging from the uterus and thus "hysterical" was applied to female problems.

The solution was successful. In a bureaucracy, if you fill out the forms, whether it is correct or not, usually the system will work.

At the conclusion of the four years of medical school and the two years of Navy doctor at the Marine base, although the experience was all in all quite pleasant, I was ready to move on. It was back to Pittsburgh for the orthopaedic residency.

4

The Great Transition

In this chapter in our road of discovery, transition is on many levels. On a personal level, it is the transition from my training as a general physician to that of a specialist—an orthopaedic surgeon.

In an expanded concept, this is the time in the history of American Medicine for the transition of specialist training from purely a surgical apprentice to that of an educated scientist clinician with academic qualifications. Formal rituals of testing of competence were emerging and directors of orthopaedic training programs were becoming professors in universities.

Finally, at this time, the early sixties, it was in the midst of orthopaedic transition into a mainly surgical specialty from what earlier was a medical specialty focused at nonoperative care of musculoskeletal ailments. Manipulation, casts and braces were giving way to surgery and metal implants.

I will take up these as phases of orthopaedic transformation. In order to give context to my personal discovery and the many unguarded moments of enlightenment, I will take a broader view and look into the development of orthopaedics as a medical specialty. How did this subdivision of surgery get its start? Why has it now grown in numbers and significance which exceeds its parent, the specialty of general surgery?

Orthopaedics Becomes a Specialty

Well, the name certainly gives no promise of the ultimate future. The first use of the word "Orthopaedia" was from a book written by an eighty-three-year-old Parisian pediatrician named Nicholas Andry. It means "straight child". It actually was written as a self-help book for parents concerning the treatment of deformity in children. The complete title was *Orthopaedia, the Art of Correcting and Preventing Deformities in Children: by Such Means as May Early be Put in Practice by Parents Themselves, and All Such Are As Employed in Educating Children*. A picture in the front of the book depicts a crooked tree with a straight stake driven beside it. There are ropes encircling the bent tree trunk, pulling it to the straight stake. The concept depicted implies progressive force can straighten the growing tree (the child). This, indeed, still is the symbol of orthopaedics. This is strange because correction now is usually by surgery. Moreover, a reasonable question emerges, why is it a self-help book? Later I will describe a reliable self-help method for correction based on therapeutic exercise.

At that time, self-help was very popular with parents because doctors were costly and had little effective treatment anyway. Transportation was very rudimentary and complex. Doctors were university trained general medical specialists with no training in the care of deformity or infection or fracture. They did no surgery. They used herbs, blood-letting and simple drugs. If a parent could avoid seeking formal medical opinion, one could also avoid the expense. Most recognized at this time that there was little useful opinion from the doctors, contrasted with grandmothers and the elders of the town. They were the trusted health authorities.

Surgeons were really a different form of physician. They usually had been apprenticed to a master surgeon, who treated war wounds and infections. War is where they learned about wound care. Another class of clinician, known as "bonesetters", looked after the fractures. Of course, the care of fractures was by closed reduction. This was a craft passed on from father to son. Finally, there was a third class of clinician—the "brace maker". This individual would fashion devices out of metal and leather to try to force deformed limbs into corrected positions. At least the brace would support the deformity. Again, it was a craft requiring no formal education, but work with the master.

It wasn't until 1780, when the first orthopaedic hospital was founded. A facility was opened up in Orbe, Switzerland, by Dr. Venel, focused on correction of deformity in a more sophisticated way with in-house brace makers. The braces were constructed for scoliosis and clubfoot deformity. Actually, little progress has been made in scoliosis (spinal curvature) with regard to bracing. As we'll see later, even here, medicine has a blind spot for better nonoperative care.

Of course, musculoskeletal ailments have always been with us. Archeologists trace the beginning of civilized humans to the findings of healed femur fractures in the skeletons of early man. The implication of a healed femur fracture is that it takes the assistance of family or tribe to survive the average of three months of immobility necessary to heal a femur fracture, even in a healthy young person. The mortality of a femur fracture in the Civil War still was 50 percent. Gradually, society did learn to provide supporting devices to allow fractures to heal. That was one phase of the beginnings of orthopaedics. The ability to apply the relatively new material, plaster of paris, to a corrected deformity was an area of expertise early developed in orthopaedics.

Even that simple device, the plaster of paris bandage—the cast—which was so important in the early history of orthopaedics, had an unexpected discovery. A military surgeon, Louis Jean Seutin, in 1835, happened to note a goat with a broken leg next to a linen starching shop. He took some of the starched linen and made a bandage, which allowed the goat to hobble on its fracture. It was the translation into fracture care for humans. It was another military surgeon, Antonius Mathijsen, who stumbled on the idea of replacing the starch, which would crumble with moisture, with plaster between the layers of gauze. Plaster was certainly a well-known commodity used in building at that time, and even in Ancient Greece and Egypt, but no one had thought of intermingling the moist plaster with gauze to allow it then to harden in conformity to the limb to which it was being applied. Such a simple idea! Both materials had been known for centuries. They had never been combined for medical purposes until the 1850s. Mathijsen was widely honored for his "invention".

That invention thus led to one of the skill areas in the historic development of orthopaedics. The application of plaster for treatment of fractures and correction of deformity, like all crafts, does take some skill and experience. This is especially true when there is a need to keep changing plaster to improve the fit for cast immobilization or to try to mold a deformity such as clubfoot into appropriate alignment. Of course, when external support systems have to be more durable, then metal and leather were used to form braces. We will have an extensive discussion about that art later on.

Of course, modern orthopaedics, as mentioned earlier, is now much more surgical than nonsurgical. Indeed, the history of surgery, itself, had some unguarded events which demonstrate how history becomes a series of unexpected accidents. As you probably are aware, as demonstrated by the barber's pole still seen at the traditional barbershop, barbers were the original surgeons. Why them? Certainly they were the ones doing it in the early Middle Ages. There is a painting in the doctor's dining room of one of the major hospitals in London showing Henry VIII awarding the parchment of craft recognition to a group of barbers. This commemorated their acceptance into the membership of guilds. At that time, long before unions, each craft had their own guild, organized to maintain quality and, indeed, preserve their turf. There was the baker's guild, the carpenter's guild, the wheelwright guild, etc. So why the barbers as surgeons? Naturally, all through the ages, both men and women needed their hair trimmed. That's one of those things which is difficult to do yourself properly. Also, to cut hair comfortably, a pair of scissors or at least a razor is desirable. In early history, much of the metallurgical craft went into the construction of military equipment in the form of spears, swords, shields, helmets, etc. One group of people who were not necessarily soldiers but used metal instruments to create useful cutting utensils were the barbers. Of course, they were not the only folks using scissors. Haircuts through the ages have been done by family members. The same was true, of course, in monasteries. In the Dark Ages, these were the repositories of intellectual activity before the development of universities. It seems that, about AD 1000, the Pope at the time, for reasons not clear, decreed that no longer was it godly for the friars to cut their own hair and thus required that people outside of the brotherhood do the shaving and cutting of hair. Thus, the barbers of the local village became privileged and were trusted with sharp cutlery for nonmilitary purposes. To these "craftsmen" also fell the job of lancing boils, removing growths and even amputations. They became skilled at bandaging as well, naturally. Thus, the red and white stripes of the barber pole.

That history of lowly beginnings is further emphasized in the historic development of medicine. Physiology and pharmacologic methodology were discussed in the early medical schools. It was prohibited by the church to do dissections and thus, in the early Middle Ages, anatomy was not discussed. The role of the blood vessels in circulation wasn't even described until the 1740s.

It was the control of infection which elevated surgery from the work of desperation on the desperate to something controllable with expectation of favorable results more likely than not. Up until the late 1800s, it was felt that prevention of infection was not possible. It was then accepted that it emerged spontaneously. Pus was felt to be good and the promotion of pus formation was thought to be advisable for wounds. It was felt that the air carried some sort of contagion, a "miasma". Thus, the first orthopaedic operations, carried out before much interest in surgical antisepsis was known, were subcutaneous tenotomies. By making a small stab wound, it was felt that the air could not reach the incised deeper tissues.

Again, it was an accident, an unguarded moment, which led to the antiseptic principle described by Joseph Lister in 1867. Pasteur, some years earlier, had described microorganisms which made grapes ferment and thus led to concepts of controlling putrefaction. Lister felt there was some similarity between decomposing foods and decomposition of flesh. Carbolic acid had already been recognized as a mechanism to stop sewage from smelling and thus he and his wife tried various formulations which would not be disruptive to living tissue but effective in controlling infection. Carbolic acid had been around for centuries but its usefulness as an antiinfective agent for humans had not been recognized. In 1867, Lister published a paper in which he described success with nine out of eleven patients. No one worried about statistical significance at that time.

Sometimes, a very reasonable idea is not yet acceptable to the current culture. A perfect example is that sad story of Dr. Semmelweis. In the 1840s, maternal mortality for births in the city hospital in Vienna was eighteen percent. Semmelweis recognized there was something about the transfer of infection in the skin when his pathology professor died after sustaining a finger laceration in the autopsy of a mother who had died of childbirth infection. By merely having the obstetricians wash their hands, the mortality rate went to one percent. Washing the hands in the peculiar culture of the times, however, was not thought to be dignified for the professors of obstetrics and thus his ideas were not widely accepted and, indeed, he became psychotic and died in an asylum in 1865.

Lister's ideas, however, were published in a reputable medical journal—*The Lancet*—and slowly became accepted, especially with the discovery that bacteria could carry infections by Koch in 1876. Now, surgery could proceed with ever-reducing rates of infection.

Of course, even with control of infections, surgery had to be very brief. Operations could only last a minute or two—the length of time a person could be held down. Only the simplest operations could be done. Finally, in 1846, however, ether anesthesia was demonstrated to be effective in a prestigious institution—the Massachusetts General Hospital—and effective surgery was born. This use of ether for tooth extraction was first used by Dr. Morton. Dr. Bigelow, an orthopaedic doctor at the hospital convinced Dr. Warren, the chief surgeon, to use it. It worked.

Still, surgery on the bones was worrisome. Surgery on the viscera, as carried out by general surgeons—gallbladder resections, stomach surgery, bowel surgery, etc., was effective because, absent the additional infection from other humans due to antiseptic techniques, the well-vascularized tissues operated upon could generally defend themselves from an infection. Bone, on the other hand, has very poor vascularity. The blood supply is sparse. This is especially true of the cortical bone, the thick bones which make the tube structures of our long bones, like the leg and the arm bones. Once infection got started in these bones, a disease called osteomyelitis developed. It was incurable. Indeed, cutting out infected bone was the major operative procedure carried out by my father, an orthopaedic surgeon in the 1930s and 1940s. Internal fixation of fractures was feared because of the very high likelihood of incurable infection. Not until the discovery of antibiotics did it become safe to do bone surgery. Here, again, accidents set the stage for events. In 1928, the bacteriologist, Alexander Fleming, noticed that a particular mold had killed a culture of Staphylococci. He published the results but didn't pursue it. He was not a clinician. Staphylococci and Streptococci are the most dangerous bacteria for bone and joint infections. At the time there was no cure for these infections. For years, nobody seemed to make the connection. Fleming's paper was rediscovered by Harold Florey in 1940 with the urgency of war. Because of the discovery of penicillin, the risks of open surgery for fractures was greatly reduced. Internal fixation and later prosthetic implantation into joints became safe.

What really made orthopaedics into a separate specialty, however, was the X-ray. Roentgen discovered X-rays in 1895. Here, again, an unexpected event, an unguarded moment, made the discovery. Various researchers earlier had noted that photographic film became fogged when a certain voltage of electricity passed through a vacuum tube. Roentgen was experimenting with vacuum tubes and was trying to develop a cardboard box which was lightproof. He passed a high-tension current through a vacuum tube in the box and noticed some nearby chemicals glowed in spite of the absence of light. Something different had happened. For reasons not clear, he put his hand between the chemicals and the tube and he could see the bones in the hand on a photographic plate. That discovery was quickly publicized and, indeed, Roentgen won the Nobel Prize in 1901. Major hospitals obtained X-ray machines within months. Only later did the dangers of radiation become apparent.

Now, with the ability to visualize the abnormalities in the bones, the arthritis of a joint or a displaced fracture visualized by way of X-rays, corrective treatment could be planned in a logical manner. With more and more experience, more opportunities emerged to solve many poorly understood problems. Fracture care became more sensible. This was especially true of the hip fracture. This was the major source of death to elderly people until a method could be created to allow them to get up. This was internal fixation. Up until surgical care of the hip was available, once an aged person sustained a hip fracture, they were placed as comfortably in bed as possible and nursed. In some cases, the fracture healed in a deformed position, leaving a painful, poorly functioning limb thereafter. Most of the cases, depending upon the age and general health of the individual, ended in death. Thus, the solution of the broken hip in the elderly made a major impact on public health.

There was one more peculiar source of knowledge which was the foundation of orthopaedics. This problem did not even come from a bacteria—it was a virus. It was poliomyelitis. Polio is a peculiar disease wherein the virus only attacks a certain cell in the nervous system. It attacks the anterior horn cell in the spinal cord. This cell, however, is vital for muscle function. It is the exchange station for all the information in the nervous system to be compressed into a single electrical signal, which goes into an extension of the cell (the axon) to meet another exchange station on the muscle. When the anterior horn cell is injured or dies, the many strands of muscles which are slave to that electrical signal no longer have direction to shorten on command. Thus the limb in which they are placed loses some function. That's what created infantile paralysis. Most of the time, however, the entire limb was not affected and some muscles survived but the limb was left with unbalanced and uncoordinated muscle activity. Once the infection from polio passed, the situation was stable but the individual was left with a semi-useless limb, which perhaps could bend but could not straighten. In that situation, the surgeons who already had experience with tenotomies (the cutting of tendons which were creating contractures) transferred these skills into the transfer of tendons from remaining healthy muscles to substitute for absent muscle function.

The reconstruction of deformity after polio became a major skill of orthopaedic surgeons. Since orthopaedic surgeons were destined to care for the deformities of all ages, they fell easily into the job of handling the deformities of the post polio patients. The majority of these individuals were youths in that the disease generally attacked young people. The more mature had developed immunity to the virus. Many of the large children's hospitals in America were developed as centers for treating polio. Many clever operations were developed, which were in the experience of the orthopaedic surgeons. This was the beginning of reconstructive surgery, which now comprises most of orthopaedic surgery.

Thus, with the skill in treating fractures, especially of the elderly, skill in correcting deformity, either in the bone or in the soft tissues as in the post polio patient, the orthopaedic surgeon has developed a separate set of skills and experience from the general surgeon or the urological surgeons or even the neurosurgeons. Thus, what was then called a "subspecialty" emerged in the teaching centers of the world.

The Pittsburgh Orthopaedic Training Program

That brings us to my arrival at a university-centered orthopaedic training program at the University of Pittsburgh. As mentioned earlier, for many years, orthopaedic training had been in the hands of prosperous and prominent senior orthopedic surgeons. My father had been trained that way. Residency was strictly an apprenticeship where you learned to do the craft by watching the master. Bakers and plumbers and carpenters had learned their craft the same way through the ages. Gradually, however, as more science crept into the understanding of musculoskeletal care, education rather than just training was recognized as necessary to achieve more progress and more effective care. Several decades before my arrival at University of Pittsburgh, the University Medical School had developed an affiliation with the Presbyterian Hospital and the Children's Hospital, which were geographically adjacent to the medical school.

Contrasted to the medical training of the nineteenth century and still present in many underdeveloped countries, it was recognized that good medical training depended upon clinical experience. The trainee had to deal with real patients. It could not be achieved just from reading the books or hearing lectures as is more or less true at many of the medical school training programs in less developed countries. Excellence in medical education can be achieved only by experiencing responsibility for care of patients as the students progress in their discovery of causes of disease, treatment of disease and hopefully, in the majority, an improvement. Clinical associations with hospitals were very necessary. Thus, university medical schools had developed various forms of association with surrounding hospitals. That's why I took my internship training at the affiliated hospitals of the University of Pittsburgh.

How was it decided who should be responsible for this training? Since the University was taking responsibility for the training, accountability as to the effectiveness of the training had to be achieved. Thus, the Director of Training had to become a member of the University faculty. Dr. Albert Ferguson was the first full-time Director of Orthopaedic Training at the University of Pittsburgh, with his salary paid by the University. In the 1950s, 1960s and 1970s, this was a growing pattern in the United States so that now nearly all the university associated specialty training programs are directed by employees of the university with academic rank.

Dr. Ferguson had been a graduate of the training programs of Harvard. He was not completely tainted in that he had gone to college at Dartmouth. His medical school and residency training, however, had been through the training programs at Harvard which, at that time, had an excellent reputation. All of the graduates knew it. Many of the pioneers of medicine and orthopaedics were on the Harvard faculty.

When I was an intern, 1957 to 1958, Dr. Ferguson had already been Chairman of Orthopaedic Surgery for several years at the University of Pittsburgh and I contacted him as to the potential for my being part of his residency program a few years later. It was recognized that I would have to put two years of service in with the Navy, but I also recognized that, to find good posts in training, one had to get in line and look for a position which would open up several years down the road. I submitted my paperwork while an intern. The selection process at that time was very simple. Only the director of the training program had the choice of who would get into the program. My Pittsburgh associations and also history of my father, though at that time deceased, were assets. My mother had also contacted the Orthopaedic Program to see if they wished to have my father's collection of the *Bone & Joint Journal* as part of their library. My selection, however, came under unusual circumstances.

Just as I was about to leave the internship at the University of Pittsburgh, I found myself in the men's room at Presbyterian Hospital on the orthopaedic floor. A very handsome man came in and stood beside me at the urinal. He looked over and said, "You're Mooney, aren't you?"

I said, "Yes, sir."

He said, "Yes, I've read your stuff. You're in."

At that point in time, we were both done, washed our hands and left. That was Dr. Ferguson and, at that point, I knew I had a place to go two years from then when I returned to Pittsburgh from the Navy. In the early history of all adventures everything is down to the bare essentials. The selection process gets much more complex as time goes on.

Dr. Albert Ferguson was a charismatic leader and brilliant craftsman as a surgeon. Several unexpected events worked together to make him successful at Pittsburgh. He was, indeed, very successful. He has trained more directors of orthopaedic departments and orthopaedic professors than any other program director. As we will see, I was one of them later on. He became president of the American Orthopaedic Association and was very active politically in the orthopaedic world for many years. He developed several operations in reconstructive surgery for children as well as serving as one of the pioneers in sports medicine. For many years, he was the team doctor of the Pittsburgh Pirates. Why did he become so successful?

The beginning of that story goes back to a discussion of the partnership between institutions of higher learning and hospitals and clinical training centers. Some of that has to do with Pittsburgh itself. In spite of its grimy history, technology and geography combined in the late nineteenth century and early twentieth century to make many fortunes. Pittsburgh sat on top of many coal fields. Coal was extremely plentiful, fairly easily retrieved from the earth and easily transported on the rivers which came together in what was called the Golden Triangle in Pittsburgh—where the Allegheny and Monongahela Rivers joined to make the Ohio River. It was easy to ship ore from the Great Lakes to Pittsburgh and thus the great steel industry grew in Pittsburgh and the surrounding area. Moreover, the first oil well was drilled in Titusville, Pennsylvania, about eighty miles north of Pittsburgh. The oil industry blossomed there as well. Steel, coal and oil were the founding pillars for the fortunes that were to be made in Pittsburgh. Andrew Carnegie made his in steel. The Mellon family made theirs in financing of oil, coal and even aluminum industries. My father had borrowed money for medical school from Andrew Mellon. The Mellons developed the leading financial institution in Pittsburgh at the time. In fact, Andrew later became Secretary of the United States Treasury. All these factors made unrestricted benevolence a possibility. A member of the Mellon family, Alan Scaife, was on the Board of Trustees of the University of Pittsburgh. It was his vision that the University of Pittsburgh Medical School would grow to be an eminent center in America. With that in mind, the Dean of the Medical School, Dr. McClusky, sent scouts to Harvard to bring in faculty. Harvard was then certainly at the top of the list of respect in many fields of medicine, including orthopaedics.

A young orthopaedic surgeon who had just finished his training and was setting up practice in Boston was Dr. Ferguson. His father had been a famous radiologist in New York

City and he had extensive connections with many other famous physicians. By his own account he was known as the "Golden Boy" in the Harvard community of orthopaedic surgeons. Why should he leave? It turned out that unexpected personal reasons forced the issue. According to his account, he thought his young, beautiful wife was becoming more than usually interested in a neighbor. It was Ferguson's view that he should move on. McClusky made a fine offer for him to come to Pittsburgh. Indeed, the Chairman of Medicine, Dr. Jack Meyers, and Dr. Henry Bahnson, the Chairman of Surgery, were attracted from Harvard. These two also became stars in their fields. They wrote extensively, made many contributions to their areas of interest and established fine traditions of training and excellence at Pitt.

There were two other factors, however, which created an environment ready for success in addition to the attraction of a very talented leader in Dr. Ferguson. Harvard had, for a long time, established a tradition of part-time professors. These were very strong, successful and experienced orthopaedic surgeons who devoted a considerable amount of time to teaching and providing free care. They were paid very little, if anything, but enjoyed the environment of learning created at Harvard. They enjoyed the pleasure of teaching, which indeed is a privilege. One can never know something better until he/she has the responsibility of teaching it to bright, inquisitive people. They ask the naïve but often insightful question which forces the teacher to really understand the subject or modify the view presented. There is probably no greater intellectual fun than dealing with an eager learner who is trying to catch up to the teacher as fast as possible in the level of knowledge. It forces the teacher to keep running faster and learning more.

With that background of the part-time faculty and the obvious success at Harvard, when Ferguson set up shop in

Pittsburgh, he made it very comfortable for the leading orthopaedic surgeons, who were already practicing, to continue their various roles in teaching, training and patient care. As time passed, he steadily moved those with less competence on. He brought along bright young stars to fill in the faculty jobs. That political skill is what determines the success of a chairman in an academic training program. Many universities have what is called a "town/gown" battle where very competent clinicians are felt locked out by the full-time faculty of the university. Competition between them emerges which, of course, is destructive to the best interests of both entities. Ferguson—"Ferg" as we all learned to call him—was able to avoid that by skillful manipulation of personalities.

The other aspect peculiar to that particular time in the history of the development of medical school was the lack of dominance of hospital administrators. At the time Ferguson arrived in the mid-1950s, the hospitals were just shifting to their new roles as teaching centers and had not developed strong administrative directors. They had the hierarchy typical of any hospital, such as a head of nursing, head of dietary, head of housekeeping. They had not developed administrators who wanted to develop programs in their own image and create mini-empires.

Actually, that phenomenon, the growth of strong, powerful hospital administrators, has been one of the sources of inefficiency of American medicine. Dr. Ferguson wrote a book, published in 1996, titled *Please Don't Get Sick,* wherein he detailed the rise of the hospital administrator and layers of bureaucracy under him. Today, when we get a bill from the hospital, there seems to be no relationship between the true value of an item or service and the charge for that entity. A fifteen dollar aspirin is the perfect example. One can seldom decipher the complex bills that arrive. That's

64

because of strong administrators in the hospital, which does not have the accountability of a profit-and-loss business. These administrators also control, to a certain extent, the income of the doctors working in the hospital. This was not the case when Ferguson and his colleagues arrived at Pittsburgh in the 1950s. They could build their practices with economic benefits as appropriate from a business sense.

Thus, the stage was set for a marvelous training program at Pittsburgh when I arrived in 1960. There was a strong, charismatic leader, financial resources were adequate and there was a vision of pride and future greatness. That last element is most vital. Pride in what you're doing is the most powerful driving force to keep the training focused at the learning process at hand. Everyone knew this was a great training program, which was going to get better. Indeed, that is the case. The University of Pittsburgh now has one of the most respected orthopaedic training programs in the world.

Surprises in My Own Training Experience

It wasn't easy and there were many surprises in the three-year residency program. Actually, it was a total of four years because I had to take a year of general surgical training before I could enter into the orthopaedic program. From my view, this was a wise assignment by the organizers of training programs. It no longer is a requirement by many orthopaedic programs. I rotated through general surgery, plastic surgeon, neurosurgery, urological surgery, etc. These were all cooperating surgical specialties with which orthopaedics would have to have an interface. In my prior training, I had had very little true surgical experience other than observing surgeries as a medical student. I was thus startled by the very first surgery to which I was assigned, when I showed up on July 1, 1960, at the Veterans Hospital associated with the University of Pittsburgh for my first assignment as a first year resident.

I was brand new, and barely knew where the operative suites were. I found the assigned operating room and, when I asked what surgery we were to do, surprisingly nobody could give me a good answer. I looked up at the X-ray on the view box and noticed it was of an abdomen but I was surprised to notice that apparently somebody had left a surgical instrument—a Kelly clamp—on the X-ray table when the X-ray was taken. After the abdominal incision was made, however, I discovered that the clamp had not been left on the table but left in the abdomen by the surgeon whom I was assisting at the time. I recognized right away that this was not the right time to ask questions. Nonetheless, the experience underlined the point that, in the craft of surgery, accidents will happen and one cannot be too careful. The surgery was completed. The patient did well and the problem resolved without incident.

The year of general surgical training as a junior resident certainly gave unusual opportunities to learn as events unfolded. As an example of unusual opportunities for learning, let me describe a small episode during that year.

Opportunities to gain surgical experience are eagerly sought after by young junior surgeons. Surgery is a skill which is part manual and part intellectual, but you certainly have to do it to get good at it—as in any craft. Thus, the Plastic Surgery Department had made an arrangement with the Western Penitentiary in Pittsburgh to service the prisoners at the location. In general, the prisoners at Western Pen were not of the dangerous type and were in the slammer for relatively short periods of time. They did have ailments, some of them peculiar to their particular trade. For instance, many of the prisoners had crooked noses as monuments to numerous fights that they had been involved with earlier. Sometimes these crooked noses did create true airway problems and were not just cosmetic impediments. Moreover, the inmates were very pleased to have a surgical procedure which would take them out of their usual routine and allow them to spend some days in the prison hospital, at which location food was alleged to be better. Thus, once a week for two months, I and a fellow resident were assigned to a clinic and a half day of surgery. At the end of two months, I had become extremely skilled at fixing noses, technically known as "rhinoplasty". We see the plastic surgeons today still advertising their skill at modifying noses into beautiful shapes. I was often quite pleased with the change in appearance I could create by straightening and puffing up a previously smashed nose. Of course, I have never dealt with fixing a nose since.

After finishing the year of general surgery, I started on various rotations in the Orthopaedic Department. In general, the rotations were four to six months in one section or another. There would be six months at Children's Hospital with pediatric orthopedics, then there would be four months with fractures, then four months with rehabilitation, etc. We only had one rotation in the area of rehabilitation at St. Francis Hospital, an affiliated institution. Rehabilitation at that time dealt with the care of chronically disabled individuals with stroke, amputations, spinal cord injury, etc. There was very little surgery involved with their care and thus it was of limited interest to an emerging orthopaedic surgeon. Nonetheless, the education was important so the trainee could experience the long-term results of musculoskeletal deformities, neurologic deficits and massive trauma. St. Francis Hospital was a very well-run, Catholic hospital. Catholic hospitals, by tradition, have been very supportive of the trainees and, indeed, there was a section of this hospital assigned to the residents which had an unusual area of delight. It had a refrigerator stocked with beer. We had our own "beer nun" that was Sr. Maria, a chubby, jolly, round-faced, Irish lady of fifty, who saw it as one of her assignments to keep the refrigerator stocked with beer and other goodies. Of course, we were not allowed to have a beer while we were on duty but, after duty, as would be appropriate for any young man growing up in Pittsburgh, a beer was a delight. Speaking of duty, we were to be in the hospital every other night and every other weekend, to take call as to emergencies and other medical problems which would arise.

Of course, this was an enormous strain on family life. My wife, Ruth, was raising two young children, a boy and a girl, who were just starting school. At that time, I was making $150 a month. Thus, we seldom could go out for any sort of recreational activity. In fact, I was usually too tired to enjoy any sort of evening entertainment. In that, everyone else in the training program was in the same boat, although most did not have children and were not married, but the burden was tolerable. In looking back, it's hard to understand how we did it but, while we were in the midst of it, we knew we were in a great project and the effort was worth it.

A Glimpse at Nonoperative Care

But now back to the theme of this story: the loss of respect for nonoperative care and exercise by medicine and orthopaedics. As I have stated, this was and still is a great training program. We all did well on our exams related to orthopaedic practice. We had learned the surgery available at the time quite adequately and, at the finish of the program, felt that we could practice orthopaedics with no limitations. This, of course, was before arthroscopy, total joint replacement and internal fixation of fractures. One of the boldest uses of internal fixation was just emerging. This was the use of rods to correct the curvature of the spine—scoliosis. They had been developed by Dr. Paul Harrington from Houston. The scoliosis surgeon in our training program, Dr. William Donaldson, had visited Harrington and, when he returned, we asked about the rods. He said he was not sure about them and would not change the method that we currently were using to correct scoliosis. That was straightening the child with a plaster cast and operating through the cast. Usually, changing traditions of care occur very slowly.

As an example, throughout the whole training program, we really didn't know the role of physical therapy. We sent some patients for physical therapy but didn't understand what was done. We knew that they used hot packs and ultrasound, massage, etc. Many of the back pain patients whom we saw in the clinics had received chiropractic care in the past but we had no idea about the rationale for chiropractic care. We knew that all of our mentors considered it foolish and quackery and thus none of us took any interest in investigating it further. It was frustrating, however, that, at that time, we had no good way of treating arthritis or significant soft tissue injuries. Certainly we did not know how to treat back pain.

Fractures were generally treated with plaster except for hip fractures, which did have implants and a prosthesis, which substituted for the fractured femoral head. We were still very fearful of infections. Braces and plaster were felt to be a significant aspect of therapeutics. We all knew that there would be more surgery in the future. We were hearing about total hip replacements done in Europe. The older doctors doubted they would work. Nonetheless, we felt we could help a lot of people with our skills at the time. In spite of our dependence on nonoperative care, we really did not have any reliable principles other than bracing.

Then came the eye opener.

A tradition in all training programs is to invite a respected clinician, a visiting professor, to spend several days visiting the program. Generally they were eminent orthopaedic surgeons from other training centers. The event was always near the end of the academic year. The project was to have the residents and even medical students present research projects to the well-qualified visitor as well as to their colleagues. He/she in turn would make several presentations in their particular areas of expertise. It was a chance for the training program to be evaluated by a knowledgeable orthopaedic surgeon who could provide perhaps some useful criticism. It obviously provided an opportunity to make a formal presentation of a year or so work product. There were usually some social events involved as well and thus it would become a high point of the year.

In the second year of my orthopedic training, Dr. Ferguson had asked his previous mentor, Dr. William Green from Boston, to be the visiting professor. Dr. Green was also an expert in children's orthopaedics and had written numerous papers concerning that area. We found out later that Dr. Green, who was about thirty years senior to Dr. Ferguson, was miffed at some aspects of a recent book that Ferg had published on children's orthopaedics. Ownership of ideas is a strange thing. Ferguson had presented various new concepts of care in the book, apparently his own. Dr. Green felt that these were basically Green's ideas which Ferguson had picked up and the book failed to give Dr. Green proper credit. Dr. Ferguson was blithely unaware of these factors on the occasion of the invitation which, as would be appropriate, was offered about eight or nine months prior to the expected date of the event.

Two or three weeks prior to the expected visiting professor occasion, however, Dr. Green sent word that he couldn't come. There was some flimsy explanation, the nature of which we never learned, but obviously it was extremely disappointing to Ferg. He called a meeting of all the residents as to what to do. Considerable work had already been done in the preparation of papers, exhibits, etc. Invitations to the faculty and resident dinner with spouses had already been sent out. On and on . . . Should we trash the whole affair? Someone mentioned the rather startling paper which had just appeared in the *Journal of Bone and Joint Surgery* from an orthopaedic surgeon otherwise unknown to us, Dr. Vernon Nickel. The work he presented from a likewise unknown facility—Rancho Los Amigos Hospital in Downey, California. It concerned successful extensive spinal fusions in post-polio patients with respiratory problems. Up to that point, this was considered an extremely dangerous operation in that the surgery was long and, absent the excellent anesthesia apparatus we have today, it was very problematic in terms of respiratory problems. Nonetheless, the results from Rancho Los Amigos, where Dr. Nickel was Chief of Surgery, were spectacular.

But there were only two weeks to go. Most busy surgeons have their schedules lined up months ahead of time. Would he be able to be here in two weeks? Dr. Ferguson knew of him from various orthopaedic meetings and called him. Yes, he would come.

I am leading up to one of those unguarded moments which changed my life. The event goes like this.

Typical of the usual drill at these events, a resident would present a case which was a successful solution of a complex problem or a new operation or some other innovation. It was ideal in those days to present the patient themselves. Patients would be staying in the hospital, often for several weeks after their surgery, and thus adequately healed to demonstrate points which were to be made.

At that point in time, bedside teaching was very common. Now, it is nearly unknown. Short hospital stays are the cause. Bedside teaching was, indeed, quite cumbersome, probably inefficient, but very effective. In a situation where there was a visiting professor, everybody involved would gather around. This would include all of the doctors on a particular service, nurses, medical students and any other interested parties. Sometimes there would be a group of twenty or thirty individuals around one patient.

It came my turn to present a lady with rheumatoid arthritis on whom we had recently done a new operation to repair her arthritic knuckles. This operation took tissue from the wrist—the tendon from the palmaris longus muscle, which has very little function—and replaced the arthritic knuckle joints with this tissue. The patient could then move the false joint easily because the painful, arthritic tissues had been removed. Such was the case with the lady I was presenting. I showed the preoperative X-rays, the postoperative X-rays, and showed her hands as she sat in her wheelchair at her bedside. We had preoperative pictures and, indeed, her hands looked a lot better and even worked better following the operation. We all were pleased with the results.

After I finished my presentation, expecting some questions as to the details of the surgery, Nickel turned to me and said, "Can she prone?" That threw me for a loop. I could barely remember whether prone meant lying on your belly or lying on your back. It's on your belly. I said I didn't know. That truly was an unguarded moment.

He said, "Well, the nurse will know." He asked who was the head nurse. Some poor lady standing in the back was pushed forward and identified as the head nurse. She said she didn't know. He then asked if the patient could straighten her knees. She couldn't. He asked if she could stand and he was told that, because she had contractures of her hips and knees, she couldn't straighten them enough to stand. He asked if the joints were destroyed by arthritis. They weren't. But I hadn't even discussed that phase of her problem.

Nickel then launched into an extensive discussion of contractures. Contractures develop about a joint whenever it is not moved through its full range. This is especially true if the joint has some inflammation surrounding it, as is the case in rheumatoid arthritis. Nickel went on to point out that these contractures which kept this woman from standing and walking could have been prevented if she had merely been instructed to lie on her abdomen whenever she was in bed. In such a setting, the knees would become straight and the hips would become straight. Gravity itself would have prevented these flexion contractures, which disabled her much more than the hand problem.

How simple!

I had not thought of that before. Nobody had discussed it before. We had been looking at a relatively minor problem for this lady, her deformed hands which still worked before the operation, when a much more significant problem had been ignored because we apparently had no solution. What an insight! I suppose now we would call it "thinking out of the box". I was very impressed. That event led me into my interest in rehabilitation, an area of orthopaedics largely ignored by most because of its chronicity, lack of sparkling surgery and overall disorganization.

I went on to finish the orthopaedic residency but found few opportunities to be involved in rehabilitation. I had the opportunity to interface with many great leaders in orthopaedics who were then at Pittsburgh, including Dr. Henry Mankin, later to become Chief of Orthopaedics at Harvard, and Dr. Tom Brower, later to become Chief of Orthopaedics at the University of Kentucky. These and many other mentors demonstrated to me the mainstream of orthopaedic care. There were some important innovations in many areas, including biochemical analysis. No one other than Nickel, however, seemed to have any interest in rehabilitation.

After I finished the residency program, surprisingly, I had no specific plans. There were some opportunities to join men in practice in Pittsburgh. Because my father had been an orthopaedic surgeon in Pittsburgh, there were some connections. All the opportunities seemed to be ordinary. Dr. Ferguson was kind enough to keep me on in a junior faculty position and had me work in the lab as well. Dr. Mankin was studying various aspects of cartilage biochemistry and I carried out some work in his laboratory as a technician more than a scientist. I didn't like it. I was getting frustrated.

One day I called a fellow, recently graduated orthopaedic resident, Shannon Stauffer. He had left Pittsburgh and gone to Rancho Los Amigos Hospital at the conclusion of training. That was due to Nickel's shrewd fishing expedition to Pittsburgh. When I called him, he said the place was spectacular. He said he had learned more there in the first six months than he had learned throughout his entire residency.

With that surprising accolade, I called Dr. Nickel to see if other places were available. Of course, that was the real purpose of his short-notice trip to our program. He said there were and that I could take over the Stroke Service. That did not sound very exciting to me, but it was an opportunity to get out of the rut that I had found myself in—and even move to California, which had been a very happy experience during my tour of duty at Camp Pendleton.

Thus, with Ruth and the two kids, in December of 1964, we were off to Downey, California, a suburb of Los Angeles.

5

Vernon Nickel and the Land of Opportunity

I started work at Rancho Los Amigos Hospital in January 1965. This was a totally new experience. At that point in time, Rancho was the largest rehabilitation and chronic care hospital in the country. It was emerging from its history as a polio hospital.

Actually, the start of Rancho was as a county poor farm for Los Angeles. During the Depression, many cities had to find some solution for the high numbers of indigents roaming the streets and slums. There was no financial "safety" net then. In Los Angeles County, on a large tract of land owned by the county, they built dormitories and built farms which were worked by people from the streets with no other means of support. In turn, they got food and shelter and a tiny income. Some of the people from the indigents of the city had medical disabilities as well. Gradually, a hospital was developed named *Rancho Los Amigos* (House of Friends).

The hospital blossomed into a major institution in the 1930s and 1940s, during the great polio epidemics. As mentioned earlier, polio generally struck children and young adults. It left them with significant musculoskeletal disabilities. These were often life threatening if the muscles involved had to do with respiration. At one time, there were forty-five iron lungs at Rancho Los Amigos Hospital. This was a device in which an individual was encased. A motor would create alternate negative and positive pressure and, by so doing, expand the lungs of the recumbent individual to create respiration. It was life saving and often an individual could recover much of the respiratory function with the aid of neuromotor reorganization which often occurs in polio patients. A few, however, were permanently encased in these metal tubes.

Working with so many respiratory problems, skilled internists began to emerge, who would develop techniques for control of respiratory problems. They were called pulmonologists. At that point in time, very little was understood about the whole issue of respiration. In addition, the mechanical devices used to assist respiration required technical support. This was not only for the iron lungs but for various testing systems such as a CO_2 analyzer, which had been developed at Rancho. It was not yet commercially available. Because of the obvious need, people with an engineering background became salaried employees of the Hospital and Los Angeles County. That great good luck gave Rancho the opportunity to be a pioneer site in many aspects of biomedical engineering.

Another peculiar advantage of dealing with respiratory polio was that it forced patient care into a team effort. The orthopaedic surgeon had to be cooperative with the internist. The mechanical engineer had to be involved with the decision making as well as the brace maker. The nurses had to understand what was going on as well as the physical therapists. There had to be good communication among all of the participants in care. It was ineffective to do this by writing and thus patient care conferences emerged. At these conferences, goals and solutions were discussed with all present so that everybody was on the same page. It sounds straightforward but that had not really been accomplished in medicine in most areas. The concept was encouraged and developed by Vernon Nickel. The team conference, with each member accountable for their area of expertise, became the core of Rancho's effectiveness. It was years ahead of its time.

The Role of the Seventh-Day Adventist Philosophy

How was it that Vernon Nickel could create such an environment of innovation? Where did he come from?

As would be expected given the theme of this book, many unexpected and unplanned events coming together led to the sparkling growth of ideas and achievements represented by Vernon Nickel's impact on *Rancho Los Amigos*.

Actually, he grew up in the Saskatchewan Valley in Canada. He went to a small Seventh-Day Adventist college in Washington State, Walla Walla College. By that time, he knew that he wanted to be a physician. An opportunity emerged for him to work at the Huntington Memorial Hospital in Pasadena and he saved money to eventually enter Loma Linda University Medical School. At that time, this institution was called College of Medical Evangelists. Now it is a highly respected medical school which also has an excellent orthopaedic residence program.

Some comment here about the Seventh-Day Adventist Church is appropriate. Their concepts had a significant impact on Nickel and, indeed, the whole area of rehabilitation.

This is a rather recently developed religion. Much as Christian Science grew from Mary Baker Eddy writing a book about her own interpretation of the Bible, Ms. Ellen G. White wrote several books in the late 1800s concerning her interpretation of the Bible. Key to the subject at hand, she considered what we would now call "clean living" as central to the faith. That, of course, meant no alcohol, no smoking and no meat. In the cafeteria at Loma Linda University to-day, you can get all sorts of burgers and meat-like dishes which are actually very tasty but are all derived from various vegetable proteins and not from any animals. Another aspect of the faith as described by White was that the true Sabbath was on the Seventh day (Saturday) and not on the 1st day (Sunday). Of course, that Seventh day Sabbath concept is the same as its Jewish counterpart.

Taking the concepts of the clean, good life into reality, various spas emerged. One of particular importance was the first in Battle Creek, Michigan. It started as the Health Reform Institute in Battle Creek in 1866. Later, it became the Battle Creek Sanitorium. It was under the direction of Dr. J. H. Kellogg. It was the forerunner to the 239 hospitals and clinics the church organization operates around the world. But what's with the cereal?

In an effort to convince the Midwestern farmers to give up their pork and gravy, especially at breakfast, these men developed breakfast cereal. At its beginning breakfast cereal was a peculiarly American solution to the meal at the beginning of the day. In Europe, it was either a continental breakfast of various pastries or, in England, bacon, eggs and ham. In the Far East, of course, it was rice.

It was J. H. Kellogg's brother, K. K. Kellogg, who, after considerable experimentation, developed a system of roasting grain to develop a breakfast cereal. The first was cornflakes. Once this system was developed, several other types of cereal were developed. At this time there was an indigent patient at the sanitarium, by the name of Post. He was being cared for for free. He became aware of the methods by which cereal was made and soon started his own system of making cereal. The first was Grape Nuts and later, in an effort to find a substitute for coffee, which was not allowed by the Seventh-Day Adventist Church, he developed Postum. When the Kelloggs became aware of this competing development of cereals, many advocated that they bring suit against Post for invasion of the patents. However, J. H. Kellogg vetoed the idea. Wisely, he recognized the concept that, the more people there were manufacturing cereal, the more widely accepted the concept might be. That's certainly a wise principle of marketing. Thus, both Post and Kellogg developed independently and flourished as we know them today.

In addition to the vegetarian-no smoking-no drinking concept, physical activity in the form of exercise was considered important to good health. There wasn't any particular formula for the exercise but it was recognized that people of good faith would not be obese but would stay healthy by diet and exercise as well as abstinence. There were a lot of irrational drugs (snake oil) being advocated then and therapeutic exercise was not advocated. Ellen White, through Kellogg, pushed it. Indeed, scientific studies have confirmed that those members of the Seventh-Day Adventist Church who abide by these principles, have an average life span of two to three years longer than the population as a whole.

Also, the Seventh-Day-Adventist-supported school, now Loma Linda, places great emphasis on the spiritual benefits of healing. That can be a two-edged sword. In medieval times, when the churches controlled hospitals, scientific concepts were often limited if they ran astray of church concepts. On the other hand, respect for spiritual aspects of life allows a more broadened view of health and disease than a purely biochemical abnormality as the apparent sole source of the problem. With that broad view, innovative ideas which are not necessarily based on current accepted scientific principles can be brought into respectable evaluation without the traditions of academic absolutism limiting them. That cumbersome discussion above is merely meant to point out a reliable principle, that innovations are often more easily accepted when strict scientific, academic principles are not the only guide of policy.

Vernon Nickel's Molding Early Experience

Nickel finished medical school about the time of World War II and found himself in Europe during much of the heavy fighting. He related to me a story which is a depiction of the clash between strongly held principles based on current "science" and the reality of an alternative concept which disobeys the principles. The story goes like this.

From an anatomic standpoint, our large bones, like the femur, have an internal channel known as the intramedullary canal. This allows the long bones to be formed into tubes which gives them the strength, based on their diameter, but they are lighter than they would be if the entire area were filled with bone. A pipe is just as strong as a rod of the same diameter if the thickness of the material at the rim of the pipe can withstand compression, but the pipe is a lot lighter. It was felt, however, that the vessels within the tubular bones were vital to the survival of the bone itself. Nature's justification for this intramedullary canal was for vascularity rather than concern of a strength-to-weight ratio.

Just before the beginning of the Second World War, a German orthopaedic surgeon, Gerhardt Küntscher, had developed an intramedullary nail for the femur. This was more or less V-shaped in cross section. That meant that the wider part was somewhat compressible. It was meant to be driven down the intramedullary channel of the femur. Such an event would obviously destroy the vasculature in the intramedullary canal. It was a very innovative thought and, although there had been some publications in Germany concerning the early experience, which was successful, certainly American orthopaedic surgeons did not accept the idea as even possible.

You couldn't tell that to some escaped pilots from German prison camps who had had their femoral shaft fractures treated with an intramedullary nail. These were young men who had broken their legs as they parachuted from the plane which had been shot down over Germany. The German doctors were not above using prisoners as a method to gain experience with various surgical procedures and this is what happened to the broken legs of the fliers. The treatment was so successful, however, that some of these brave young men escaped the camps or were exchanged and ended up in the military hospitals of the American forces in England.

In spite of what the orthopaedic surgeons had been told by their mentors concerning the impossibility of this form of treatment, an X-ray was taken of a pilot who had escaped from POW camp. He was in a hospital in England and it was seen that it worked. The fracture was obviously healed and in appropriate alignment. Lacking any description of the procedure or illustrations of the device, the X-ray only gave a tantalizing hint of its true nature.

But this happy pilot was anxious to return home and any thought of delay to retrieve that femoral rod, which, of course, was the desire of the orthopaedic surgeons, was unacceptable to him. One of the doctors, however, came up with a "brilliant" idea. There was just a touch of scientific credibility to his idea when he said to the young man that the doctors were unaware of the nature of the metal in the rod. Because of the war effort, the rods probably had significant impurities in them. We are aware that some metallic impurities can affect neurologic function as well as sexual potency. That's what got the pilot's attention. When he was told that the problem of sexual potency could be avoided if he would just have a small operation to remove the rod, there was no further discussion, no need to delay. The rod was retrieved the following day. The pilot went home very happy and probably his wife was happy as well.

Nickel went on to write a significant paper on the effectiveness of femoral rodding in the early American experience, but it took at least another fifteen years for it to be accepted as mainstream care. For many years, those relying on the unsubstantiated principles of potential vascular damage by the rod insisted it wouldn't work in spite of overwhelming evidence of its efficacy. His papers were disregarded. Preconceived, current "scientific" principles are hard to give up. Another way of putting it is that "you can't argue with a closed mind."

At any rate, eventually Nickel returned from the war years and had an orthopaedic residency, first at the University Program in Iowa, and then later at the famous Campbell Clinic in Memphis, Tennessee. At that point in time, the Campbell Clinic was the most significant orthopaedic training program in the country and had many of the leaders in the field practicing at this very healthy and skilled group practice in Memphis. Following the program in Tennessee, Nickel then joined a flourishing orthopaedic group practice in Los Angeles. It had been going on for about fifteen years before he got there. It was started by Dr. G. Moser Taylor, a Seventh-Day Adventist. Taylor developed several instruments which are still used in surgery today, such as the Taylor retractor.

Nickel Takes Charge of Rancho Los Amigos

As is true of any young clinician starting in practice, he wasn't overly busy. An opportunity was offered to him by a former classmate at Loma Linda University—Dr. John Afeldt, who was then medical director of Rancho Los Amigos Hospital. Rancho at that time was overwhelmed with polio problems and Nick was invited to organize the Orthopaedic Department. This was in 1953. That was both good and bad news. Just as the Chinese character for disaster and opportunity is the same, often the worst of circumstances can become the best of circumstances.

The problems of medical care in this setting were overwhelming. The numbers of polio patients were far more than could be cared for by any single person. Moreover, the income derived from county salaries at Rancho Los Amigos was meager compared to the available income from private practice in the community. It would take an unusual person to be willing to work at Rancho Los Amigos.

Nickel had several solutions. One, he recruited female orthopaedic surgeons. The first was Jacqueline Perry, in 1955, who was a classmate of his brother at University of California San Francisco. She had been a physical therapist before going to medical school and finishing the orthopaedic residency. She was ideally suited for being involved with post polio care. Moreover, as a single young woman, she did not have the significant financial needs typical of an orthopaedic surgeon trying to support and educate a family. Later, in 1957, Alice Garrett joined the team at Rancho. The other innovation was to recruit residents from the training program at USC. Being a county hospital, Rancho Los Amigos Hospital was in partnership with the Los Angeles County General Hospital, also a county hospital. As was the case in Pittsburgh, the training program was supervised under the auspices of an academic department, in this instance the University of Southern California.

There were not enough residents in that training program to cover all the needs at Rancho Los Amigos, however.

Because the experience was so unique, Nickel was able, with his great powers of persuasion, to convince various directors of training programs around the country to send their residents for a rotation at Rancho Los Amigos for six months. These were from training programs such as Northwestern, Baylor, Harvard, Loma Linda, UC Irvine, etc. Still, there was not enough staff to supervise all of these residents and to provide the appropriate stimulus for training. To solve that, Nickel turned to part-time program directors, who would be willing to work part-time for the meager salary of the county physician. In trade for that, however, they would be able to direct a particular service, treating a specific disease entity, which provided them probably the largest body of experience in the country. If a young person wished to develop a reputation of academic achievement, it could be most easily achieved in this format. In that it was only a part-time job, they could participate in a general orthopaedic practice simultaneously and generate a reasonable income. That was the situation that was going on at the time that my friend and fellow resident at Pittsburgh, Shannon Stouffer, went to Rancho Los Amigos in 1964 to take over the spinal cord injury service. Nickel offered me a similar position in 1965, to take over the stroke service.

What an opportunity! Or was it? I had never before treated a stroke or head-injured patient from an orthopedic perspective.

How Do You Treat Something Never Seen Before?

Both Shannon and I had sixty beds of patients with a single disease entity, all being treated in the team method. In that, by the time they came to Rancho, the patient no longer had the acute phase of the problem which required day-to-day decision making, the goal of their time at Rancho was to be rehabilitated. That means try to gain the most of the residual function left after the acute problem had stabilized. The goal from a social standpoint, of course, was to get them out of the institution, into the community and, hopefully, as independent as possible so that they could start generating income on their own. It was for the purpose of reducing the number of institutionalized, chronic care patients that Los Angeles County at that time was so generous in support of Rancho Los Amigos Hospital. It was a unique intersection of understanding of need and financial availability. Just as in real estate location is everything, in scientific progress often timing is everything.

To demonstrate the power of gaining experience with a large number of patients with essentially the same functional problems, such as paraplegia, quadriplegia, hemiplegia, I will provide several anecdotes.

When I arrived at Rancho, I took over the stroke service from Jacqueline Perry, who was starting a different service. She was the first orthopaedic surgeon who had ever been in charge of stroke rehabilitation—I was the second. Because of that unusual perspective, several reconstructive surgeries were developed, many of them designed to make the patient more mobile, to allow them to be freed from braces and to improve cosmetic appearance. Some were borrowed from polio reconstructive surgery. Because of the experience gained at the stroke service at Rancho Los Amigos Hospital, three years after starting to work there, I was giving an instructional course at the annual meeting of the American Academy of Orthopaedic Surgeons on stroke rehabilitation in terms of the principles of physical rehabilitation and the reconstruction surgery available. I had statistics in terms of hundreds of patients and various operations done on twenty to fifty patients with one-year follow-up. No one had ever published such an extensive experience before. I was only three to four years out of my residency and thus it was a marvelous privilege. It initiated my entry into academic orthopaedics although, at the time, that was the furthest thought from my mind. I had no intention of becoming an orthopaedic professor.

But there is a problem if experience becomes too unique. Were the surgeries developed really orthopaedic surgery? From my standpoint, they were. They were essentially tendon transfers and releases, which had some similarity to polio reconstruction. This type of reconstructive surgery was well-accepted by the orthopaedic community. To do the procedures correctly, however, one had to have a clear understanding of the goals of the procedure and the preoperative and postoperative rehabilitation treatment. At a place like Rancho, that could be accomplished, but it was seldom available to the general orthopaedic surgeon practicing in a community hospital. Here is an example.

A typical deformity of somebody who has suffered a stroke or hemorrhage into one side of the brain is an abnormality called hemiplegia. In this situation, the upper and lower extremities on one side of the body are operating largely under reflexes and have limited control from the brain. The area of the brain which normally would control their movement has become disabled. In the case of the lower leg and foot, the muscles to pull the foot up are stronger on the inner aspect of the foot rather than the outer aspect. The operation developed to correct that was to cut half of the tendon (the anterior tibialis) and move it to the outer side to balance the upward pull of the anterior tibialis. Thus, even though working on reflex activity, the foot functioned rather well. This often allowed the individual to get rid of the brace.

The problems about reflex deformity are somewhat more significant in the upper extremities. A typical deformity based on reflexes is the arm held bent at the elbow, held at the side. No matter how hard the person "wills it", they cannot straighten the elbow. The reflexes for the flexor muscles are stronger than the extensors. This problem can be simply remedied by a small procedure done under local anesthesia, where the musculocutaneous nerve which controls the biceps and brachialis muscles (the forearm flexors) can be injected with phenol. This partially disables the nerve but does not kill it. There is still some residual function but not as much as before and thus the arm can reside in a more relaxed posture at the side when standing. For a surgeon knowledgeable of the anatomy, this is a fifteen-minute procedure in that the musculocutaneous nerve is conveniently near the surface between two muscles and easily identified.

Years later, my brother-in-law had a cerebral hemorrhage which left him hemiplegic. He had good rehabilitation care but he had the very bent arm deformity about which I published a paper in 1967, describing how to fix it with a phenol injection. No one in Cincinnati had apparently ever heard of that or was willing to do it. He did get Botox into the muscle but that supplied only temporary relief and wore off in six months. There was not even a billing code for phenol injection. The procedure had fallen between the cracks. It was too specialized for what was considered perhaps too small a problem to everybody other than the individual burdened by it.

The point of this discussion is to demonstrate how the environment of extensive, unique experience and the absence of limiting guidelines allows advances in concepts. This environment only works if the leader of the operation, Vernon Nickel in this instance, is secure enough to allow ideas which are not his own to emerge. He recognized that, in some instances, leadership meant getting out of the way. It is not that he did not have a passion for what is right and wrong, he merely recognized that people have to learn through their own experience and, his experience being different, he might have alternative solutions for a problem. This willingness to accept other ideas was nicely demonstrated once at a conference at Rancho.

Typically, on Friday afternoon, we would have a medical conference. It was usually directed by one of the program directors and thus focused on a specific problem such as a spinal cord injury problem, scoliosis problems, pediatric deformity problems, etc. I remember specifically one occasion where Nickel was describing a proposed solution for a complex surgical problem and, after he had finished with what was thought to be a very reasonable idea from my standpoint, Dr. Perry got up and presented a ten-minute discussion of why the whole idea wouldn't work. She was a very detailed, specific, straight-thinking woman, who made her points with telling accuracy. At the conclusion, Nickel summarized the discussion where she had just put down the boss in no uncertain terms, as follows: "Perry, it's not that I mind you being right. It's that you're so goddamned right."

My First Experience in Challenging Conventional Care

Nickel was also smart about managing people. He recognized the potential for burnout. Therapists could only stay on one service for a year. After that, they had to rotate to a different service so that they would not fall into a rut concerning solution of problems. The medical directors of programs were frequently rotated for the same reason. In my case, a new, bright, young leader was emerging and, to make room for him, Nickel reassigned me to be the director of the Problem Fracture Service. Thanks to the orthotic service (brave shop) and my recognition based on earlier research that function applied to the healing fracture was a positive rather than negative event, we had developed what was called a fracture brace. This was to treat certain fractures of the femur by walking on them with the support of a brace rather than keeping them immobilized in a spica cast. As mentioned earlier, there was considerable resistance in mainstream orthopaedics to carrying out femoral shaft rodding.

In the late 1960s, there were many beds at LA County Hospital populated by patients lying in spica casts. These were put on after weeks in traction. That's a cast which immobilizes one leg to the knee and the other leg from toes to chest. It is a large nursing care problem. Many of these people, therefore, could not be cared for at home. They were often kept in this situation for as long as six weeks for relatively simple femoral shaft fractures, longer for more complex fractures.

Having developed a cast brace, we reported the experience of 100 consecutive patients with femoral fractures treated in this manner. They were compared to fifty treated in the standard spica manner. Ninety-eight percent of those treated with the cast brace healed, whereas only seventy-five percent of those treated with the spica healed, and the healing time in that situation was two months longer than with the cast brace. There were six refractures in the spica group, but none in the cast brace group. Bone healing guided by function is stronger. Even the chief of orthopaedics at LA County Hospital could not believe the statistics. Thus, a Problem Fracture Service was developed at Rancho under my direction. It was becoming progressively more inconvenient to treat the femoral fractures with the cast braces at the downtown hospital known as LA County, which was fifteen miles away by progressively more clogged freeways. The downtown hospital is now known as LA County/USC Medical Center. It is a marvelous structure which often appears as the hospital in the background on television shows and soap operas concerned with the drama of hospital events.

The Problem Fracture Service at Rancho allowed us to work with all sorts of materials other than plaster to develop supportive devices. Here is another unguarded moment! One day, a general practice physician from England showed up with a shoe insert made of a relatively new plastic known as polypropylene. One of the problems of plastics used for orthotic devices at that time was their potential to fail because of fatigue. Any material applied to support a living person is going to be under constant demand of various mechanical forces, such as bending and straightening. Many plastics will fatigue and break as occurs when you bend a wire repeatedly. Polypropylene would not. If you see a plastic hinge on a small item such as a jewelry box, it is made of polypropylene. It gets stronger with every bending motion.

In that this clinician had developed this for a short insert for painful feet, we started working with the engineers and developed a vacuum form system so that we could make a brace which fit the contour of the leg. It was molded so that it was light, strong and cosmetic. This was called a plastic AFO (ankle-foot orthosis). These are now very common but the original ones were first developed at Rancho at the Problem Fracture Service. Again, because of the availability of brace makers and biomechanical engineers, and recognition of the medical need for a lighter, more supportive cosmetic brace, the AFO was developed. Experts with different points of view working together made it happen. We published the details of the technique. It is now the standard for bracing.

As in any institutional program, there is always the problem of space and personnel. As discussed earlier, the need for medical treating personnel, to a certain extent, was solved by the rotation of residents from other training programs. Although the directors of the various programs were part-time, the basic work of the operation was carried out by residents. The whole mechanism of treatment was engineered by the treating team conferences as discussed earlier. If there were insufficient residents to do all of the work, then the director of the program would have to do it. Nickel was smart enough to keep the number of residents slightly less than the number needed to carry out the jobs of the various programs. Thus, the program directors competed for the interest of residents, who could choose in which program they wished to serve their two to three months during their six-month rotation at Rancho.

That competition for residents became a particular problem for me when I was expecting to enlarge my Problem Fracture Service. The director of the Problem Back Service left to become a medical missionary. That service was in an area next to the Problem Fracture Service. I planned to take over the space. The psychologist working with that program, however, recognizing that his job was in jeopardy if I converted the space to a Problem Fracture Service from a Problem Back Service, made a particular effort to educate me as to the fascination with the psychology of pain. Thus, on the basis of his urging, I took over the Problem Back Service.

How Do You Make Chronic Back Pain Interesting?

The Problem Fracture Service was handed over to another clinician and I had the job of recruiting eager orthopaedic surgeons to treat chronic back pain. That's a

91

challenge! Most orthopaedic surgeons hate to see chronic back pain. Even today, there is poor understanding of why it's there and how to treat it. One thing is clear, after they have had four to five operations, a sixth is very unlikely to be of benefit. Such was the case of many of our patients.

Because I was now in charge of forty beds of chronic back pain patients, several innovations had to be developed. Because the problem of back pain was so similar in all of them in terms of its location, when there were forty patients, it was hard to keep the clinical problems straight. Therefore, I had all the patients fill out pain drawings, which helped to clarify their problem from their neighbor's. These drawings were a simple front and back outline of a human form. At the top of the page, there were various types of symbols which were used to depict different attributes of symptoms, such as numbness or stabbing, or pins and needles. The patient was asked to place the symbols on the full page, front and back human form outlines. These pain drawings have continued to be a very serviceable item in treating orthopaedic pain problems. Each new patient in my office, even today, fills out a pain drawing, and then, when they return on each occasion, they fill out another pain drawing, which allows the clinician to identify changes in their status. Frequently, patients will not fully verbalize location and intensity of pain and the drawings are very helpful to clarify these issues. Such drawings are now widely used throughout the medical community. Some of the residents rotating through the Problem Back Service wrote some papers regarding these pain drawings. Certain aspects of the pain drawings can be converted into psychological insights. It becomes a rather short MMPI test. Trying to understand how and why individuals depict their pain is a fascinating insight into the psychology of distress. One can sometimes even identify those who are faking pain.

Also to encourage interest of the residents and to gain some insight as to where the pain could be coming from, we had the privilege of using the fluoroscopy unit at Rancho Los Amigos Hospital. At most hospitals, the turf of the Radiology Department is tightly guarded. Only the radiologists can use the equipment. With the freewheeling attitude at Rancho, given appropriate training and credentials, anybody could use the fluoroscopy unit. The internists were using it to develop skills with catheterizations. Nickel's brother was a radiologist and advised on the organization of the Radiology Department at Rancho. Thus, when I proposed that we, the residents and I, start injecting each other under fluoroscopy to evaluate pain sources, there were no administrative barriers.

We took on a project which became the source of numerous resident papers. Under fluoroscopy, using hypertonic saline, which is essentially seawater, we started injecting the facet joints of the spine. This fluid is slightly irritating. You will recognize this if you've ever had an open cut and have gone for a swim in the ocean. The facet joints are easily defined radiographically as the joints on either side of the spinous process, which control the degree of rotation of one vertebral segment on the other.

We made some interesting discoveries. Injection of a small amount of fluid into the facet joint would cause referred pain to the buttock. A little more would cause pain into the buttock and the thigh, and a little more would cause pain in the buttock, thigh and calf. This is known as referred pain. The little human experiment documented that the amount of irritant (in physiologic terms known as "noxious stimuli") can affect the brain's perception of the amount of pain. None of this pain is carried by the peripheral nerves feeding the particular area but it comes from stimulation to certain segments of the spinal cord. The pain could be abolished by local anesthetic injection. One could not tell which level was injected by the location of the pain. We finally published this experience in 1976.

All of these were new observations. They became available because of the opportunity to use equipment (the fluoroscopy unit) seldom available to orthopaedic surgeons. Also, because there was a group of eager young learners anxious to understand the phenomenon of pain and willing to work on the project. None of the residents involved in the program, which lasted for several years, resisted the idea. They were just as fascinated as I was as to how you could make the pain come and go. We injected the disc and found the same phenomenon. Later on, this form of investigation, injecting into the discs or facet joints, grew into a whole subspecialty, currently known as pain management. Now it is usually carried out by anesthesiologists but occasionally by physical medicine doctors and occasionally by radiologists. Very seldom are orthopaedic surgeons involved in this form of investigation and treatment. It all started in the Fluoroscopy Unit at Rancho Los Amigos Hospital. Only because there were no administrative barriers and the pleasure of new insights could it have happened.

Another Example of the Unguarded Moment in Innovation

Although it may appear somewhat oblique to the main theme of this book, my discovery of more effective nonoperative care, a few more instances from my experience at Rancho would be useful to demonstrate how an environment comfortable with new ideas such as Rancho can lead to new discoveries and new insights. The unguarded moment can be converted to new knowledge.

As mentioned earlier, the directors of various programs at Rancho, known as "services", would be rotated. This was an effort to supply fresh insights to mechanisms of treating complex problems. For a while, I became director of the Amputee Service. The initiation of the Amputee Service emerged by, once again, an unexpected event—an unguarded moment.

There was a well-known Polish orthopaedic surgeon named Marion Weiss, who had developed a rehabilitation hospital outside of Warsaw. Even in the late 1950s and early 1960s, Rancho Los Amigos was known through the literature as an eminent rehabilitation hospital. Dr. Weiss had, in Polish, at the entry to the hospital and above its name, the words "Rancho Los Amigos of Poland".

Dr. Weiss was an unusual personality. He was very courtly and presented himself with old European manners. He came from a noble family which could trace their heritage back a thousand years in Poland. His brother was chief justice of the Soviet-controlled Polish government after the Second World War. He stayed at our house several times. My wife was overwhelmed at their first meeting when he bowed and kissed her hand. No one had ever done that before. He usually wore a tapestry vest, encasing a moderately rotund potbelly. He spoke excellent English.

At one of the conferences at Rancho, Dr. Weiss presented his statistics concerning the immediate postoperative fitting of amputees. This, again, went against all of the current principles of wound care. Imagine this—you had just amputated a person's leg below the knee. You closed the wound. Then you wrapped the leg up in plaster, put a pipe with a shoe at the end onto the plaster and asked the patient to start walking on it the next day. At that point in time, it was still considered an important factor for early wound healing that it be undisturbed. Early motion to the wound was thought to be destructive and would lead to failure of healing.

Nonetheless, using this technique, known as "IPOP" (immediate postoperative prosthesis), his success in rehabilitating below-knee amputees was remarkable. Frequently, fitting the standard prosthesis had been delayed six months to a year in the practice then. That was because often a contracture at the knee developed. Also, the stump remained edematous (too much fluid in the tissues) and there would be significant atrophy if they were fitted with a standard prosthesis. Thus, partially for economic reasons, fitting was delayed until there no longer was edema and all the atrophy had occurred. It would be very costly to keep fitting the standard prosthesis every one to two months. Yet, in Dr. Weiss' series, they were usually fit with the standard prosthesis within two or three months. They did not require refitting. By the time they had walked on their IPOP prosthesis, there was no edema and the tissues were functioning under normal mechanical stresses so there was no atrophy. Because the prosthesis was made of plaster, it could be changed frequently. The prosthesis went above the knee to the midthigh so that it held the knee in a straight position, preventing a flexion contracture from developing. Because the prosthesis encased the lower thigh, some of the load of body weight was transferred to the walls of the prosthesis above the knee. The individual, of course, started out walking with crutches so that immediate full weight-bearing was not necessary. They gradually, however, discarded the two crutches, progressing to one crutch and to cane and then to not using anything. It was rehabilitation at its finest.

Marion Weiss, on one of the occasions of presenting his series, described how he fell upon the idea. It turns out, as would be expected in any conflict, following the war, there were many people with traumatic amputations from land mines, explosions, etc. Usually the amputations had been treated under emergency conditions and, although the wounds were healed, they were left with painful scars, making prosthetic fitting extremely difficult. Thus, following the war, many people needed revisions of their amputations. Such an event occurred at Dr. Weiss' hospital (Konstantion). A certain young man was scheduled for revision of his below-knee amputation, which he, indeed, needed because he could not be fitted with a prosthesis. Lacking a prosthesis, he really could not be involved with any type of meaningful work. Just before the amputation, the young patient told Dr. Weiss that he had to leave the following day to get married. This was a surprise to Weiss who said that that really would not be possible. The young man pleaded with him and stated that, if he were not there, the intended marriage would be off and he would lose a woman who had waited for him through the war and whom he dearly loved.

In that plaster, as mentioned earlier, had been a standard material available to orthopedic surgeons, and not knowing what else to do, following the revision amputation, Weiss put some gauze over the surgical site, wrapped the leg in a fabric material known as "stockinet" and applied plaster, encasing the below-knee amputation in plaster up to midthigh. He applied a broomstock to the end and gave the man crutches. He was indeed able to leave the following day.

About two weeks later, the young man returned to the clinic. He had revised the broomstick to a certain extent and applied a shoe at the end. Wearing long pants, he really didn't look too unusual. He seemed happy. Fearing the worst, the cast was removed. To everybody's surprise (except the patient), the wound was very nicely healed. There was no swelling, no infection and the incision was relatively painless for this short time following surgery. All were startled. Nonetheless, noting the success with that single patient, the technique with various slight modifications was applied to a large number of patients, mostly getting revisions of traumatic amputations. This was the series that Dr. Weiss presented at Rancho.

At Los Angeles County, there was a different problem. Diabetes is an extremely common entity, especially in the indigent population, which filled the clinics at LA County Hospital. Poor diabetes control, poor hygiene and obesity all lead to the development of nonhealing wounds and gangrene in the feet of diabetics. The only solution when that occurs is an amputation to an area where there is sufficient blood supply to achieve a healed wound. This, however, was a different set of patients than the more or less young significant vascular disease.

Nonetheless, with the assistance of the Orthotic and Prosthetic Department of Rancho Los Amigos and a modification in the mechanism of doing the amputation so that the more vascularized skin of the back of the upper calf was brought to the front, covering the end of the tibia, we started to do a series of amputations at Los Angeles County Hospital. We did fifty consecutive below-knee amputations in diabetics. They all healed and were successfully fit with prostheses. They did far better than a similar group treated the usual way. Up to that time, that was the best track record ever published. It, indeed, documented the power of function to heal wounds. At first, it was very poorly accepted by surgeons and clinicians in general, but the facts spoke for themselves. The fitting and revision of the IPOP prosthesis and fitting of normal prostheses afterward became the function of the Prosthetic Service at Rancho, which I directed. Incidentally, another benefit of early function was that none of the patients developed phantom limb pain. This sometimes occurs when fitting is delayed a long time.

The whole thing would not have occurred if Dr. Weiss had not deviated from surgical traditions to accommodate the urgent bridegroom.

Weiss added another method of care, which had a short history, deleting it from current medical practice for non-medical reasons. This was Weiss' springs.

Dr. Weiss and Dynamic Fracture Fixation

A not unreasonable idea for the treatment of spinal curvatures is the application of a dynamic force to achieve correction. Before the Second War, a Czech physician (Dr. Gruka) had published some papers on correction of spinal curvature (scoliosis) by surgically applying springs from one rib to several ribs below this. X-rays had been published but the work was not continued due to the war. Weiss took up the idea, however, and applied it to compression fractures of the spine. In a compression fracture, the front part of the vertebral body is mashed down but the back part of the vertebral body, including the facet joints, is intact so that the deformity that occurs is a bending forward of the spine. As long as the facet joints are intact, there is stability resisting displacement when the spine is rotated.

When Weiss came to Rancho on one of several occasions, he brought a movie (no videotape yet!). The movie showed an auto accident which had just occurred in Warsaw. Then it showed the victim of this accident being brought to the emergency room and the camera focused on the date and the clock on the wall. Then the camera focused on the injured patient himself and on the X-rays that showed a compression fracture at the base of the thoracic spine, which was quite significant. The camera then showed a segment of the surgery with reduction of the compression fracture and application of a spring with hooks at either end, which were applied to the lamina on both sides of the spinous process.

The lamina is strong bone which connects the spinous process to the facet joints. The spring was about $1/2''$ in diameter and came in various lengths. The wound was closed and, the next day, as evidenced by the calendar on the wall, the patient was standing at the bedside. Two days later, he walked out of the hospital with the use of crutches.

Again, this was a very dramatic demonstration of rehabilitation and mechanisms to achieve early function.

We started using Weiss springs at Rancho Los Amigos. They were not appropriate for many spinal fractures but they were, indeed, marvelous for compression fractures. A particular patient of mine, who emerged from my private practice in Downey, California, was a wrestler on the high school wrestling team. He was involved in an auto accident and had a compression fracture which mashed about half of the height of his top lumbar vertebral body (L1). The standard of care at that time would have been to reduce the fracture and fix it with rods. The rods would have been placed two segments above and two segments below the fracture. Thus, five segments of the spine would have been immobilized. That's an impossible loss of function for a wrestler. You all have seen the contortions that are necessary for wrestling. I had been on the wrestling team in high school myself and really understood his problem. I operated on him and applied the Weiss springs. The fracture reduced and went on to heal. The injury had occurred in August. Wrestling is a winter sport. He competed that year and actually became the county champion in his weight class. Obviously, he had normal flexibility. We used the springs for several other categories, such as Scheuermann's disease, where, because of some vascular abnormalities, the front part of the vertebra does not grow normally and there is forward curvature of the spine. It worked marvelously well for that as well.

So where did it go? Nobody uses it today. It turns out that the manufacturer of the Weiss springs was the Zimmer company. Due to some design problems and some misunderstanding of the metallurgical needs, some springs broke prematurely before the fracture or deformity being treated had completely resolved. This led to several lawsuits against Zimmer, which they lost. In that the market for these devices was rather small, rather than losing any additional money, Zimmer took them off the market. Weiss springs have not been available since the mid 1970s. It was a good idea destroyed for the wrong reasons.

And what happened to Dr. Weiss? This is another example of a good idea destroyed for the wrong reasons.

In those days, in the early seventies, Russia still controlled Poland. It was a time of intrigue and fight for political power. As is often the case of a successful entrepreneur of ideas, Weiss had developed some political and professional enemies. It was a time of political intrigue. While staying at our house, he would get telegrams from back home, which would have apparently innocuous comments, such as "Aunt Mary is sick and will soon need medical attention."

"Aunt Mary" was a code word for the hospital. His associates at home were telling him to hurry home because some administrative action was to take place which would unseat him as director. He stayed at our house on three different occasions and, each time, various similar telegrams would arrive, forcing him to return prematurely. He enjoyed the fountain of ideas at Rancho and, of course, it was a mutual exchange of concepts as demonstrated by a few of his achievements described above. Nonetheless, the world was quite troublesome at home.

About 1976, we got word that he was found hung from a lamppost outside his house—an apparent suicide. We knew that to be wrong. Actually, Dr. Weiss made a very religious man and carried with him a Bible, which he read every day. He was extremely patriotic to the best interests of Poland and hated the Communist control. He hated most of the bureaucracy which prevented many innovative procedures and imagination. Unfortunately, as demonstrated by his achievements, he was an activist. He was active in the political underground, trying to undermine the Soviet control. Apparently that activism caught up with him in a disastrous way. Who knows what further achievements could have occurred if he were permitted to continue his work? While staying with us, Marion Weiss gave us a lot of insight as to the pride and patriotism of the Polish people who historically have been bent in many directions by conquering powers, but have never been broken as a culture.

Now, just one more example of the unguarded moment is appropriate here before we move on.

Rehabilitation through the Skin

One day an engineer from the nearby North American Aviation plant showed up in my office at Rancho. He had in his hands a glistening piece of what I thought was black plastic. He told me it was vitreous carbon. North American Aviation was trying to solve the problem of re-entry from space. It was known that, in the case of a vehicle returning to Earth's atmosphere from outer space, tremendous temperatures would develop. No metal known could withstand these temperatures. It was believed at that time (and still is) that some form of ceramic would better withstand the heat. The material, vitreous carbon, is made under tremendous heat and pressure from carbon. It can be made in any sort of design. In the processing, however, it loses about twenty percent of the volume. The end product is extremely pure, hard carbon which won't react with anything. The engineer brought with him collar-button pieces of vitreous carbon. He had the idea of implanting them in the scalp of bald men and allowing the protruding carbon to be snapped onto a toupee. I guess that's not a bad idea but it was not the road I wished to explore.

On the other hand, there was a real need to achieve skeletal fixation of a prosthesis when the amputation stump, either upper arm or below knee, was very short. It was very difficult to fit a usable prosthesis on a short stump. It was difficult to gain suspension—the ability for the prosthesis, the artificial limb, to stay in place. If there was a mechanism by which we could implant a rod into the bone and have it protrude through the skin without getting infected, then we could develop a snap-on prosthesis.

There was no previous work on this and there were no guides. Nonetheless, it seemed feasible in that this new material had already been tested for its biologic reactivity. Indeed, there was none. I even had one of the collar buttons implanted into my arm, where it protruded for two and a half years. It never got infected. I only lost it to a water polo game with my son.

We also tested various designs in a most unusual manner. At Rancho, there was a group of patients being treated for pressure sores secondary to paraplegia and quadriplegia. Lacking sensation, they had developed infections due to constant, unrelenting pressure. The treatment for this was to place them recumbent with the pressure off of the infected area until the wound healed. Indeed, these were perfect candidates for the evaluation of skin reaction to various materials and design.

We informed them of the reason for the research—in this case to develop direct wire connections with their muscles through plugs which we could place on the skin. Of course, they were interested. In that they had no skin sensation, we could operate on them without even the need for local anesthesia. Thus, in a group of six paraplegics who had to be lying in bed anyhow, we implanted four different designs of plugs protruding through the skin. Some were with vitreous carbon and some were with silicone. Out of this experience, we did find the ideal design.

We tried the design on several amputees. At this time, bone cement had not yet been developed and so we used a porous ceramic into which the bone would grow to attach to the bone and had the rod protrude through the skin of the stump. In the research for this, we found how far bone would grow without supplemental vascularity from the side. We found it to be 1 mm. Unfortunately, the mechanical trauma at the skin interface was too severe and we never got a long-term, secure, infection-free closure, although all did well initially. The fixation to the bone, however, was secure. No patient had a long-term problem but all of the four devices implanted had to be removed. This obvious need has not yet been solved.

On the other hand, as to the connection for muscle stimulation, we were successful in fitting a young man with a below-elbow prosthesis which had an array of plugs in his skin. There were wires which led to muscles in the forearm. The electrical signals from these muscles were therefore carried to the plug in the arm, which then, by a plug in the prosthesis, went to small motors in the prosthesis, which controlled the hand. It was a unique achievement. It was even written up in *Time* magazine with a picture. The plugs never got infected.

Unfortunately, unknown to me, the patient chosen for this operation was a drug addict and mentally unstable. He committed suicide about a year after the surgery.

Due to the complexity and expense of the whole operation, it was not pursued thereafter. And speaking of expense, what happened to Rancho and Dr. Nickel?

It Is Time to Go

In 1975, Proposition 13 passed in California. This froze property tax rates. Property tax had been the main support for county financial resources. Because of that, up to that time, the county hospitals and Rancho Los Amigos had few financial strains. After passage of that proposition limiting use of property taxes, the strains grew seriously. As usual in these circumstances, changes happen slowly. Recognizing the decrease in funds available for engineering research, many of us left Rancho. Shannon Stouffer left in 1976 to become Chairman of Orthopaedics at Southern Illinois. I left in 1977 to become Chairman at the University of Texas Southwestern. Nickel left several years later to take a position with the Veterans Administration in Washington. He was responsible for the development of various rehabilitation programs in the United States at the VA Hospitals. Even though he was very adept politically, he gradually became frustrated with the bureaucracy of the system and finally took a position at UCSD, directing rehabilitation at Sharp Hospital.

Even here, as his life wound down, there was an unnecessary unguarded moment. By 1996, Nickel had more or less retired. He was seventy-four. He was a large man and had been moderately obese. As the years passed, he developed spinal stenosis. This is an ailment where the overgrowth of bones in the spine narrows the area available for nerves. Eventually, the tunnels through which nerves proceed outside of the spinal canal (neural foramina) are too small.

Because of that, when the individual walks very far or stands too long, the legs grow weak and numb. The blood supply to the nerves is squeezed. This was progressively a problem for Nick. Eventually, he had surgical care at UCSD for decompression of these nerves. I was cosurgeon at this procedure. It was done successfully.

Because of his age, he was not taken from the Recovery Room to his own room but was placed in the Intensive Care Unit, where his vital systems could be monitored. Here's where, even in our modern age of technology, a weak link can allow destruction of the chain of effective care. It seems, in the early morning hours, while lying on his back in a sedated manner, he could not get rid of his secretions in the mouth and had a blockage of the throat. The medical phrase for this is "he aspirated". It was recognized by the monitoring equipment and could be corrected by merely rolling him onto his side or stomach so that the secretions would not impede respirations. He weighed 260 pounds. The nurse in charge of the area weighed 110. She couldn't move him. Finally, she got help to move him but he had been without oxygen for several minutes. He had drifted into a coma.

When we got there early in the morning, all of his vital functions were doing well. The problem, however, was that his brain wasn't working. When his brain would ever recover was greatly in question. The neurologist in charge wanted to keep him on life support indefinitely. Recognizing what a vital, enthusiastic, independent person Nickel was, I argued against it and urged the treating doctor to take him off life support. He said, "No." Finally, his son, who was also an orthopaedic surgeon in Northern California arrived. He, against Dr. Nickel's wife's desires but based on my urging, agreed that he should be taken off life support. Nickel would not want to be a dependent vegetable. That ended an era.

106

6

The Clash of Physical Therapy Concepts

In 1977, I submitted my resignation to Rancho Los Amigos and agreed to take a job as Chief of Orthopaedics at Parkland Hospital in Dallas, and Chairman of the program at the University of Texas Southwestern. I was to go there in October. I had really not planned to go to Dallas and had assumed that I would be Chairman at USC since that job had come open also in 1977. A rich resource for the Orthopaedic Training Program at USC was Orthopaedic Hospital. This was a private hospital which started as a children's hospital approximately forty years earlier by Dr. Lowman. It had a very strong endowment due to the poignant aspect of chronic care related to children's musculoskeletal disability. A year or so earlier, I was at a meeting in London, England, and was walking across London Bridge with a longtime colleague, Dr. Gus Sarmiento, who at that time was Chairman of Orthopaedics at University of Miami in Florida. We were talking casually and he asked me what was new in Los Angeles. I said the news had just come out that Orthopaedic Hospital had received the largest private donation (at that time) to any orthopaedic program in the country. A widow, whose name was unknown even to Orthopaedic Hospital, had donated eight million dollars for research. I remember Sarmiento saying, "Oh, yeah?" and that was the end of it. It turns out that, in the competition for the USC position in 1977, recognizing the financial potential, Sarmiento had applied and made a good case for a new approach compared to somebody who was already on the USC faculty. I lost my bid to be chairman and he got it. Now, that's an unguarded moment!

The McKenzie Impact

I only bring up the story to put the timing in perspective. I was a lame duck at Rancho. Nonetheless, the programs would continue. One of the therapists on the Problem Back Service told me about a physiotherapist in New Zealand who had published some material about treating patients with back pain by exercising them in extension. That means bending backward. Up to that time, the only exercise program which had any credence in the physical therapy and even the orthopaedic world was bending forward. It was thought that one could straighten the lumbar lordosis. Lordosis is the natural curvature of the low back. Reduced lordosis at that time was thought to be of benefit to back pain patients. Too much curvature (lordosis) was thought to pinch the nerves. No research had ever supported this view but it was more comfortable to do sit-ups than to arch backward. Out of curiosity, I encouraged Kathy, a physical therapist on our service at Rancho, to contact McKenzie. She had told me about his different approach, and therefore invited him to put on a seminar at Rancho. At that time, we had adequate funds to cover the trip. In contrast to the usual opinion then, he proposed that backs should be treated with arching backward to improve lordosis, not flexion in most cases.

Robin McKenzie showed up and was prepared to evaluate our patients. He was a delightful man—exactly my age.

He spoke with a New Zealand accent, which seems to be a cross between South African English and British English. His phrases were very entertaining.

However, when he evaluated the patients on the Problem Back Service, he found a type of problem not seen before. He had never seen patients in New Zealand who had had three to four back operations. These were really chronic pain people with social problems in addition to their medical problems. This was his first visit to the United States and he certainly wished to demonstrate his style of back treatment in a positive manner. He was very discouraged. He recognized that the stage in tiny New Zealand (population 4.5 million) had significant limitations to his new idea.

After two days of ineffective treatment to our patients, he could not change their pain. His method usually achieved rapid changes. He turned to the group of therapists, nurses and others and asked if someone had a back problem. Several did and he examined them, told them to do certain exercises and asked them to return the following day. To everybody's surprise, on the following day, all of these "patients", who were actually on the staff on the Problem Back Service, indicated considerable improvement. There was something there. That brought me to the question of why the McKenzie techniques were not used everywhere.

That really brings up the credibility of physical therapy techniques. How did McKenzie get this insight? It's a real demonstration of the unguarded moment.

McKenzie was working as a physiotherapist. Again, only in the United States is the profession known as "physical therapy". In the rest of the world, these practitioners are called "physiotherapists". I will explain why later. He was a graduate of the then only physical therapy school in New Zealand at Otago University. It is in the South Island in the college town of Dunedin. Dunedin is Celtic for "Edinburgh", after which the New Zealand city of Dunedin modeled itself. Many of the streets are named and oriented just like in the Scottish city of Edinburgh.

After graduation, he was doing standard physiotherapy work in Wellington, New Zealand. This included a lot of massage and manipulation. He even initiated the New Zealand Manipulative Therapy Society. This was done to defend themselves from the chiropractors, who were beginning to emerge in New Zealand. They were trying to project themselves as the exclusive experts in manipulative therapy. He was president of the society for several years.

On a particular day, he had instructed a patient to lie on the examining table while he was caring for another patient. The head of the examining table was propped up and the patient, who McKenzie later called "Mr. Smith", not having any particular instructions as to how he should lie, did so lay face down, thus arching his back backward. Mr. Smith lay that way for perhaps ten to fifteen minutes until McKenzie had finished his other activities. When Robin turned to the cubicle where Mr. Smith was reclining, he was horrified to see him in what was then thought to be an inappropriate position. At that time, everyone knew that flexion of the spine was the way to treat back problems. On the other hand, when he asked to get up, Mr. Smith said, "Thank you. I haven't felt this good in months." Nonplussed, McKenzie said, "Right. Come back tomorrow and we'll do it again."

That event must have happened thousands of times before. For reasons that are not clear, nobody else thought it was important. McKenzie, recognizing that this positive result was not supposed to happen on the basis of current knowledge, began to explore it further. The more he explored the concept, the more effective repeated extension exercises became in his experience. He gradually developed a scheme for evaluation of repeated movement to end range with the patients both standing and recumbent. He discovered another phenomenon now known as "centralization of pain". Repeated motion in certain planes, usually simple back extension but sometimes extension with the pelvis displaced laterally to one side or the other, would cause the pain in the leg to retreat and go to the center of the back. He recognized that, when that occurred, successful treatment with that exercise usually resulted. If the pain went further down the leg, that was not the appropriate exercise and an alternative strategy should be undertaken. If the pain could not be centralized, treatment by repeated motion would be ineffective. Later, considerable research has verified these observations. Based on these observations, McKenzie wrote several books and recently he has published a two-volume textbook with extensive references. But, then it was news and nobody else did it.

Now, here's the defining moment. He convinced his wife that they should refinance their house for him to get the money to visit physiotherapy experts around the world to learn if these concepts were being used elsewhere. He was a great salesman. She was convinced and he took six weeks off.

This was 1967. As he explained later,

> . . . growing up in isolation, we tended to leave New Zealand with an in-built relief in the superiority of European and American expertise. At the time I was sure that, in the great centers of medicine, they would know far more than a modest practitioner in a small British dominion. Their highly researched methods would help me get a better appreciation of where I was headed in treating the more resistant problems occurring in the back and spine.

His initial visits were to Vancouver and Boston, where he had connections. "I found doctors practicing one routine for all patients, regardless of symptoms and they were all following a nonspecific approach. Physiotherapists were living in a degree of ignorance that projected a poor image in medical circles." He, indeed, was appalled that no one seemed to feel any responsibility for improving the treatment of back pain. In the United States at that time, physiotherapists were not allowed to use manipulation and were reduced to accepting patients from general practitioners and specialists for treatment by ultrasound and hotpacks, which were currently in vogue.

McKenzie then went on to Oslo, where he visited a well-known physical therapist by the name of Freddy Kaltenborn. He had earlier taken courses in chiropractic in Germany and in osteopathy in London. He had worked with a manipulative orthopedic practitioner in London—Dr. Cyriax. What was impressive to McKenzie on the occasion of visiting Kaltenborn is that he had developed a training program in manipulative therapy. He had succeeded in winning over the government and securing funds for spinal manipulative therapy. He was developing higher standards of treatment for back and spinal disorders. He had set up a sophisticated teaching and accreditation organization. It was a system of education that, McKenzie, himself, would later seize upon. But, to his surprise, neither Kaltenborn nor his fellow professionals had any awareness of the centralization phenomenon or of its predictive value. No one had seemed to notice the centralization phenomenon. On the other hand, the message of institutionalization of a training program had a lasting effect on McKenzie.

In Paris, he approached the leader of the French Manual Medicine Association—Robert Maigne, who was carrying out entirely osteopathic principles and had no room for revolutionary ideas. He, too, had no idea of the existence of importance of centralization. He treated physiotherapists as technicians who were there to follow the instructions of the physician. McKenzie was learning that the physicians really had no better knowledge of the appropriate treatment than he did.

On he went to London and discovered that even the great Dr. Cyriax, who was doing manipulation, had no awareness of centralization. He turned a deaf ear to McKenzie's attempt to acquaint him with the concepts. The British physiotherapists had no knowledge of centralization but also were unwilling to listen to McKenzie's ideas. Those working at St. Thomas Hospital, one of the greatest teaching hospitals, were unaware of the effects of using repeated end range movements for assessing and treating back problems. He found it hard to accept the blank looks that appeared when he tried to tell them that repeated movement would cause the pain to centralize. They were used to carrying out manipulation and paid no regard to the effect of how it changed the pain. It didn't bother them that manipulation sometimes made the pain worse.

After all this experience, he was confirmed in the importance of his findings. He recognized, however, that he had to develop his own theoretical concepts and had to pursue this himself. He had learned that he was ahead and alone in his branch of healing. Moreover, with proper evaluation, definition and organization, such as he had seen in Norway, he could turn his hand to exposing his concepts and methods to all involved in New Zealand. He had uncovered an important link in the chain of understanding back pain. He felt an urgency to make sure that others learned what to look for and what to do. Thus, his willingness to make the great effort to come to America and, starting at Rancho Los Amigos, carry out educational programs.

Because I was impressed by his ability to effectively treat patients, when I moved to Dallas, we started a research project to demonstrate the efficacy. We compared McKenzie-type evaluation and exercises to what was then a popular traction method to flexion exercises. The McKenzie program was highly effective and, for those who had failed treatment with the other two groups in the research project, it was likewise effective. We finally got around to presenting this in 1986.

But why was this exercise program effective?

Massage or Exercise

This leads us into discussion of physiotherapy and the balance between active, independent exercise and manipulative therapy where someone else is doing the "exercise" in the form of joint movement. It is a very basic question which still has not been solved today in a practical sense. How much of each of these forms should be reimbursed by health insurance?

Where did formalized, therapeutic exercise get started? As usual, we can turn to the ancient Greeks. At that time, medical treatment had a religious aspect to it and physicians were often connected with temples. In that setting, the word "exercise" is loosely translated from the Greek to mean "freed movement". This was to be followed by relaxed bathing. Obviously, exercise would be hindered by garments and thus should be performed in a state of undress—the Greek word for this is "gymnos"—and the enclosure where it is performed is called the "gymnasium", where lack of garments was expected. Hippocrates recognized that the absence of exercise would lead to atrophy and liability for disease and quicker aging.

Formalized concepts of therapeutic exercise remained dormant until the early nineteenth century, when the concept of medical exercises and the thought that "movement cures" began to develop. This seems to be formalized by a Swedish fencing instructor who had been exposed to German military calisthenics. He developed a system of free exercise routine, which was described to be in harmony with the whole body. In 1813, Ling obtained a royal license to open the Central Gymnastic Institute in Stockholm, calling it the Ling System of Swedish Movement. It also included Swedish massage. One of the students of the Ling System was a medical student named Gustav Zander. In 1857, Zander became a part-time teacher of gymnastics at the Swedish boarding school. Medical gymnastics as taught by Ling required almost constant attention from a personal trainer and thus Zander looked for a more economical alternative. He eventually combined levers, wheels and weights into a series of machines and called his system "Medico-Mechanical Gymnastic Method". Zander opened his medical-mechanical institute in 1865. He used twenty-seven different devices for active exercise, wherein the patient would move the machine. Many of the machines were equipped with a performance monitor to register the force of exertion. This provided a mechanism to measure exercise. He later went on to devise a total of fifty devices, some using externally powered machines.

Zander had been licensed in medicine in 1864. By 1880, he was made lecturer on medical gymnastics at the Medical School of Stockholm. In 1892, the Society of Swedish Physicians gave him its semi-centennial gold medal in acknowledgement of his eminent works in the domain of mechanical-therapeutics. In 1896, he became a fellow of the Royal Swedish Academy of Science. His devices were exhibited widely in various international exhibitions such as the Universal Exhibition of Philadelphia in 1876, Brussels in 1876, Paris in 1878, Stockholm in 1897, Berlin in 1899, Paris in 1900, and Santiago in 1901. On all occasions, the devices were awarded gold medals.

These devices marked the beginning of the separation of free exercises, such as are used today in the form of barbells, Swedish balls, elastic bands, etc., and exercise machines which isolate certain movements and can vary the resistance. These are the devices present in every health club in America now. As of 1906, there were ninety such institutes around the world (Russel, Schwartz & Company 1906: The Leading Teachers of Dr. G. Zander's Medico-Mechanical Gymnastic Method).

But why, with all the documentation of achievement described above, has the equipment designed for Zander not persisted in the medical treatment of musculoskeletal problems? Actually, the idea died with the growth of hospitals, antisepsis, and the apparent benefits of prolonged rest. We will discuss this later but this has a lot to do with medical politics. As the great hospitals emerged in Europe and America, there was no room for sweating exercisers. Rest and passive care were considered far more effective. Why work up a sweat exercising if you can be made better with passive care and various modalities of electrical stimulation, etc.? As we will see in the paragraphs to come, the expectation of magic in emerging technologies was far more attractive than some brief episodes of hard work.

Meanwhile, graduates of Ling's Swedish Gymnastics Institute were much sought after. In 1870, the Education Act was passed in England, which was an enabling device for broader education, including remedial gymnastics. Ling graduates were entrusted with training England's first generation of women gymnastics teachers and later they began to form a professional physiotherapy organization.

A component of Ling's system was therapeutic massage. It was gaining support as a worthy treatment on its own. A French Surgeon, Lucas-Championniére, was the first to elucidate the value of massage as a follow-up of orthopedic surgery in bone setting. He published a treatise, titled "Massage and Mobilization in Treatment of Fractures", in 1889. This was based on his observation that a broken arm bone in one of his patients had healed both faster and stronger than expected, despite not being immobilized after injury. He described mild massage to the surrounding soft tissues, stating that pain typically disappeared more rapidly, swelling was reduced and recovery of function was accelerated. The older method of total immobilization inevitably produced stiff joints. His methods were in contrast to the popular care of fractures in England at that time until actually the 1950s, which was, indeed, prolonged immobilization. Thus, up to this time, massage was becoming accepted as therapeutic, as was progressive motion.

The lack of fully trained and accredited personnel led to an interesting commentary on human nature. The individuals carrying out massage were known as "rubbers". In 1890, the *British Medical Journal* published articles noting that many of the locations where massage was supplied were really houses of ill repute and their employees carried names like "Nurse Dolly" and "Nurse Kitty". They were "nothing more than prostitutes masquerading under the cloak of massage." To counterbalance that, ten respectable masseuses in 1895 started a trained nurse's club in London and formed a society of trained masseuses. There were few male masseuses or rubbers at that time. That was essentially the beginning of women providing ethical musculoskeletal care with appropriate education and certification.

New Technologies and Health

In addition to exercise and massage, another phase of modern physical treatment is the use of electrical energy. Surprisingly, the input of a Seventh-Day Adventist institution had a role here. At Kellogg's Battle Creek, Michigan, sanitarium, it was recognized that intelligent diet, natural medicines and sunbaths were important therapeutic agents. This will be discussed in more details later. Due to its northerly location, there was short supply of sun in the winter months. Thomas Edison had just devised the light bulb and, in 1891, Kellogg came up with an artificial light bath cabinet. A paper was presented at the newly formed American Electro-Therapeutic Association in 1894. The sanitorium shortly had full body cabinets which were equipped with 60-watt incandescent bulbs and mirrors. This was known as "heliotherapy" and was used for treatment of lumbago, rheumatism, jaundice, etc.

A more significant component of electrical energy as a passive therapeutic component for modern physical therapy came from a very unusual source. Nikola Tesla, a Croatian who had immigrated to America and initially worked at the Edison Labs, suggested in an American scientific journal that currents of high frequency were capable of increasing body temperature without obvious deleterious effects. That led to the development of diathermy and later ultrasound.

Incidentally, Edison and Tesla had a falling out. Tesla developed the idea of alternating current, which allowed long distance transmission of electrical power. Edison, on the other hand, did not believe that that would be successful and maintained that direct current would be the most useful method of transmission. Because resistance in the wires was much more to direct current, power stations to boost the power had to be present every several miles. Tesla developed many other projects and eventually he was bought out by Westinghouse. He later died a pauper in New York City. Edison Labs grew into the General Electric Company. An engineer from the General Electric Company, Professor Elihu Thompson, presented a paper at the American Electro-Therapeutic Association in 1894, demonstrating scientifically the benefits of diathermy.

One other aspect of modern physical therapy needs to be explored. This is hydrotherapy. It also goes back to Greek and Roman days, where baths were thought to be therapeutic, sometimes alternating between hot and cold plunges. It was thought in the 1800s that hydrotherapy could wash out through the skin pores whatever bad stuff was causing disease. There was no scientific support for this, however. It slowly drifted into mainstream medicine, and a former Confederate Army field surgeon, Simon Baruch, experimented with hydrotherapy as a method to control fever. Eventually he applied it, treating patients with chronic disease at Montefiore Hospital in New York. He was elevated to Professor of Hydrotherapy at the College of Physicians and Surgeons at Columbia University after publishing a book in 1889, called *The Principles and Practice of Hydrotherapy*.

How Did American Physical Therapy Get Started?

Thus, we now have all the tools of modern physical therapy in place—exercise, massage, electrical energy modalities and hydrotherapy. How did they become converted into a profession? Here the name of Mary McMillan emerges as significant. Although born in Massachusetts, her family moved to England and, in 1906, she enrolled in a two-year graduate course in physical culture and corrective exercises at the Liverpool Gymnasium College, where Ling gymnastics were taught. She also took two years of training at the Royal College of Surgeons in London. She then became in charge of massage therapy at the Liverpool Southern Hospital. There she worked under the famous Dr. Robert Jones, who is identified as the father of modern orthopaedics. He, indeed, was the nephew of a bonesetter, Hugh Owens Thomas, who was the first physician in a dynasty of Welsh bonesetters. Bonesetting was a craft using manipulation to not only treat fractures but also arthritis. With that background, shortly after Britain entered World War I in 1914, she became Director of Orthopaedic Rehabilitation for the British military service. She was quick to grasp the value of physical rehabilitation in treatment of men felled by compound fractures, amputations, etc. Because of the dangers, she was urged to come home by her American family. She became Director of Massage and Medical Gymnastics at the Children's Hospital in Portland, Maine.

With America's entry into the war in 1917, Surgeon General William Gorgas (of yellow fever fame in Panama) was assigned the job of developing reconstruction therapists. He investigated what the British and the French had been doing. At that time, there was no system available to carry out any rehabilitative treatment. A Dr. Frank Granger, Assistant Professor of Physical Therapeutics at Harvard and President of the American Electro-Therapeutic Association, was assigned the job. He organized a group known as "reconstruction aides". These were to be unmarried women between twenty-five and forty. Men were needed to serve in the military. Mary McMillan, with her unique background, was assigned to be the organizer of the reconstruction aides.

As the war wound down, the Surgeon General's office, under whom the reconstruction aide program had functioned, made plans to disband it. McMillan and several other colleagues were convinced that there was a place for the skills which they had developed. She initiated a national organization. It gradually developed into the Physiotherapy Association and its journal, the *PT Review,* had its first issue in March of 1921. McMillan would also write a textbook: *Massage and Therapeutic Exercise,* which became the standard text for physical therapy training. It was also first published in 1921. As exemplified by the title, hands-on therapy was the superior therapeutic mode to exercise. That concept is supported by the reality that the title for a book which provided the history of British physical therapy, published in 1995, is *In Good Hands.* One of the themes of the whole discussion in this book is the reality that current physical therapy has more enthusiasm for the manual and passive aspects of physical treatment than the active exercise.

Oh, yes. How about the name? In the late 1930s and early 1940s, a new specialty of medicine known as Physical Therapy Physicians was emerging. They had contested for several years their proprietary right to the term "physical therapy" because the physiotherapists were, at that time, known as "physical therapy technicians". The M.D.s decided to change their name to "physiatrists" and the American Council on Physical Medicine declared itself in favor of that designation. This choice was a reflection of the fact that, with emerging information, the use of physical agents was no longer limited to treatment but these doctors used a wide range of diagnostics and medications as well. The old name, Physical Therapy Physicians, was inappropriate. To assure verification of status and their own area of turf, the American Physiotherapy Association polled the forty-four chapters and rapidly reorganized the name to the American Physical Therapy Association. They were no longer technicians.

Physical Therapy—Hands-On or Hands-Off?

That brings us back to the philosophic clash that Robin McKenzie brought to the field of worldwide physiotherapy and American physical therapy. His treatment advocated largely a hands-off program of exercises. Patients were evaluated and instructed by therapists in the appropriate exercises. They were observed and corrected. The same treatment didn't fit everyone. The therapists acted much as coaches in the treatment of patients. The patients were expected to take over responsibility for treatment for themselves. The use of electrical modalities, massage and hydrotherapy was disregarded. These were the main tools of usual physiotherapy. When I first understood it, I thought, *What a concept!* Get the patients to heal themselves. Only in extremely recalcitrant patients is manipulation by a therapist necessary. The responsibility is with the patient. Whenever they are in trouble, they can treat themselves. McKenzie wrote two books for the public on the subject of spinal treatment, called *Treat Your Own Back* and *Treat Your Own Neck*. They sold more copies to the public than any other publication regarding self-treatment. That resonates a little bit with another self-treatment method, where the word "orthopaedics" was coined by Ambrose Pare, as we mentioned earlier.

Because the treatment depends upon a structured evaluation, which leads to a specific exercise program, a rational conceptual framework can be developed. McKenzie courses are now taught around the world by physiotherapists using exactly the same formats and materials. They are now at five levels: A, B, C and D and a fifth level which uses the same principles as applied to the extremities. The McKenzie program is the only physiotherapy technique which is taught at university postgraduate level. It is a master's program at Otago University in Dunedin.

Now, here's the irony which demonstrates the resistance to a reasonable idea. When Otago University wished to open a clinic to supply patients for treatment to allow training for advanced McKenzie therapists in 2002, one would think naturally there would be resistance from the community physiotherapists. There was none in Dunedin. No therapist in Dunedin was using McKenzie techniques. Indeed, only five therapists in the Dunedin community used any form of exercise therapy. What is so ironic is that McKenzie, a graduate of the school in Dunedin, has now become internationally recognized as a great pioneer in physiotherapy. His stature was recognized when he was awarded the very prestigious Order of the British Empire. Amazing! No one in the city where he trained was using his techniques.

7

It's the Vision Thing—Is It the Personality or the Idea?

We have just discussed the story of Robin McKenzie, who deviated from traditions of physical therapy into an area which nobody else had apparently developed or explored. He used exercises which were identified by a standardized clinical examination, but largely carried out by the person with back or neck pain themselves. He discovered that, everywhere he visited, physiotherapy was a hands-on type of program with massage and modalities and manipulation to treat pain. No one else was using a specific program of exercises because he apparently was alone in these concepts. He persisted, though he realized he would be ridiculed for concepts which were not traditional. The concept now is alive and well and growing internationally. His persistence was validated. To what degree is that success due to the personality versus the validity of the idea?

That is not an easy question to answer in the world of medical care, where there are so few mechanisms to identify success or failure—other than persistence of life or failure with death. If an engineer goes wrong building a bridge, everybody knows it's wrong when the bridge collapses. In medicine, where there are so many factors related to good health, pain and persistence of disease, a new idea may fade or prosper due to unpredictable factors.

Thus, this is a good time to bring up two important personalities in the field of nonoperative care. They were rough contemporaries. These two totally diverse physicians were John Harvey Kellogg, the medical director of the Kellogg Sanitorium in Battle Creek, Michigan, and Andrew Still, the founder of the first osteopathic school in Kirksville, Missouri, in 1892. He started the entire field of osteopathy. What in the world could these two very different individuals have in common?

Again, to keep us on track with the story, this is a description of the journey toward better understanding of rational, nonoperative care for the musculoskeletal system. Also, it is a description of nonsurgical maneuvers available to enhance and preserve health. Under that broad heading, these two individuals deserve recognition and an important place in this journey of discovery.

The Heritage of J. H. Kellogg and the Church

Let us first turn to John Harvey Kellogg. We touched on Kellogg—actually, when first mentioned, it was his brother, K. K. Kellogg, who developed breakfast cereal. They were Seventh-Day Adventists. The influence of the Seventh-Day Adventist Church was depicted as an important aspect in the experience of Vernon Nickel and the development of Rancho Los Amigos Hospital.

Here, additional background relative to the Seventh-Day Adventist Church and its relation to Kellogg is necessary. This brings us to Ellen White. She is an important figure. Indeed, she is perceived by the church as a prophet.

How did that happen? Now, this is truly an unguarded moment. One afternoon in 1836, a nine-year-old girl named Ellen Harmon (Ellen White's maiden name) was "playfully" attacked by a group in school and somebody accidentally threw a rock at her head and knocked her unconscious. She also had considerable bleeding. She eventually was carried home by her friends but was unconscious for several weeks. She also had considerable facial disfigurement and was not accepted back at school by her classmates. She was unable to concentrate and couldn't breathe through her nose because of the injuries to her face. She therefore did not return to school until after the third grade.

She became self-educated and proceeded into the ability to write. Indeed, she wrote over 100,000 pages in longhand, twenty-five million words. She wrote more serious books, published in more languages, with wider distribution than any other woman in history. She wrote in areas in which she had no formal education and no experience. Her publications relative to education became mainstream at Columbia Teachers College and Cornell University—respected institutions in this area.

Regarding medical events, she wrote volumes recommending specific simple rational methods of therapy. She spoke out strongly against tobacco and called it "a poison most deceitful and malignant". In 1864, exactly 100 years before the famous Surgeon General's Report, she said it was poisonous and could cause birth defects—later confirmed by other studies.

The head injury apparently caused a cerebral setting for visions. In 1861, she predicted precisely the event at Fort Sumter which would start the Civil War. Three days before the San Francisco earthquake in April 1906, she had a vision describing specifically the event and location. Because she was involved in the Adventist movement and had a deep commitment to the Bible, her visions relative to spiritual aspects and health were accepted by her colleagues in the church. By the time she died in 1915 at the age of 87, she had recorded over 2000 visions relative to the future of the church and health aspects. These were recorded in multiple publications.

Specifically as related to health issues, on June 5, 1863, about two weeks after the formal organization of the Seventh-Day Adventist Church, Ellen White, concerned with her husband's health, had a vision about the broad principles of healthy living and she was instructed to present this divinely inspired message to the Seventh-Day Adventist Church. She wrote down the principles of healthy living in 1864 in a book called *Spiritual Gifts*. She also read books by various health reformers of the day and recognized that her vision was largely in harmony with the emerging thoughts from these doctors. In 1865, during a vision in Rochester, New York, she received additional information, indicating that the Adventists should have an institution of their own to teach and practice health principles. These concepts included five basic principles. They were a balanced diet, which she interpreted to be a non-animal diet. They included the use of natural remedies such as pure drinking water, fresh air, sunlight, exercise and absence of harmful things such as tobacco, alcohol and drugs. Preventive medicine was important to care for the body as the temple of God (I Corinthians, 6:19–20). Also included was mental health, which was basically recommendations for positive thinking and, finally, spiritual health. This meant service to others and promotion of happiness. With these principles, the first educational institute, called Western Health Reform Institute, was opened in 1866.

So where does J. H. Kellogg come into this story? It turns out that a John Preston Kellogg, his father, who had recently moved to Battle Creek, Michigan and started a broom factory, was approached in 1864 by a member of the emerging Seventh-Day Adventist Church to contribute to a needed medical institution. They had a concept of improved medical care with a spiritual basis. Many of the health idea were those developed through the visions of Ellen White.

When approached by the Church, John Preston Kellogg said he would contribute $500 to seed the new institution. At that time, in his broom factory, he made seventy-five cents a day. Nonetheless, he made this pledge out of anger against the then-current medical care available. They had earlier botched medical care and caused the death of his beloved wife and their infant child.

Actually, his concepts were justifiable. At this point in time, in the mid-1800s, medical care was a shambles. The medical lore was to do such things as treat an earache by blowing tobacco smoke into it. To treat skin itch, apply water and soap with a corncob, followed by a lotion of lard and sulfur or gunpowder. To stop a nosebleed, the patient should chew on newspaper or hold a dime on the roof his mouth for a few minutes, etc., etc. On the other hand, the advice of the Church, which was crystallized in an 1863 vision of Ellen White, was to have a balanced diet of non-animal foods. The use of natural remedies, such as pure water, sunlight, rest and exercise and the absence of anything harmful, such as tobacco, alcohol and drugs, was advocated. An important part of medical care under the Adventist healthcare system was prevention. This was not a concept current in American medical care at that time. As described earlier, prevention would be achieved by proper exercise, sleep, nutrition and avoiding harmful drugs. Mental health was important and focus on positive health habits was necessary. Of course, spiritual health was likewise important with the concept of physical health being achieved by loving service to God as well as man.

On the basis of this early financial support, the Western Health Reform Institute opened its doors on December 5, 1866. Hydrotherapy was an important area of treatment.

They had hot and cold baths, etc. It became clear, however, that physicians in line with the view of the church were few and far between. Thus, one of John Kellogg's sons (he had sixteen children) was sent to the Hygieo Therapeutic College of New Jersey. He then attended medical school at the University of Michigan and later further education at Bellevue Hospital in New York. John Harvey Kellogg became a surgeon.

When he returned to Battle Creek, he was appointed medical superintendent of the institution in 1876 and, in 1877, Kellogg changed the name to the Battle Creek Medical and Surgical Sanitorium. He chose the word "sanitorium" to emphasize cleanliness.

It should be pointed out that this was just about the time that Lister identified the germ theory and the use of antiseptic surgery.

By 1885, the Battle Creek Sanitorium was the largest institution of its kind in the world, and had 15,000 patients a year. It was, indeed, a sanitary place where emphasis on washing hands and freedom from contamination was important. At the time far ahead of its competing institutions, it had a mortality rate of one patient per thousand.

In spite of the focus on preventive medicine, John Harvey Kellogg was a significant surgeon. He did his 20,000th abdominal surgery when he was eighty-four with a mortality rate of less than one percent. At that time, the average mortality rate was over ten percent for abdominal surgery. He did this by the application of the health principles of Ellen White—absence of drugs, healthy diet, appropriate rest and exercise. Exercise in this context was general physical activity, not an organized program.

Kellogg carried out many reforms. At this particular time, the corset was advocated for women's styles. He felt this was unhealthy and decreed it should be abandoned in all women working at the institution. Based on the visions of Ellen White and the Bible, he advocated vegetarianism. He believed in exercise and was aware of equipment developed by Gustav Zander, whom we will talk more about later. His concept, however, was that exercise should enhance blood flow, not necessarily enhance muscle strength. Nonetheless, he developed a dynamometer, which was a strength-testing device. In 1907, this was purchased by the U. S. Naval Academy and was used for the next twenty-five years to establish the capabilities of cadets there. He had great enthusiasm for the value of light and developed arc lights to stimulate the skin. He developed a mechanical horse (used by President Calvin Coolidge) for daily exercise. He thus was a well-known medical personality in the mainstream and his publications were respected. The dominance of the sanitorium at Battle Creek was well-known. He became one of the early advocates of preventive medicine in the form of healthy habits, positive mental and emotional attributes and, in this setting, with significant spiritual support.

Was the success due to his overwhelming personality? He was a true leader. Was it due to his ideas which, as time has shown, were very rational and reasonable and certainly are used today in the realm of positive health care? Due to the impact of his concepts, however, Loma Linda University was developed and many healthcare institutions around the world as well. The ideas were good and the personality was powerful. Which was more important?

Osteopathy and Andrew Still

That leads us to a discussion of Andrew Still. Andrew Still was the son of a doctor, who also was a Methodist minister. He had been treated by the many methods of care available in the mid-1800s. At that time, there were, of course, no antibiotics. There was not even a rationale for when medicine should be used. It was felt important that, to get rid of bad toxins, one should vomit or defecate as much as possible and so various agents which would create diarrhea or vomiting were commonly used. Doctors at that time frequently prescribed whiskey for sedation as well as opium and morphine. They often prescribed mercury-based drugs without any real justification. Blistering was thought to be a positive health event.

Like Kellogg's father, he had reason to react against the current medical practice. Still had lost four children to the medical "care" in the mid-1800s. Although he had been a physician and surgeon in the Civil War, he observed the inadequacies of medicine at that time. Being a deeply religious man himself, in 1872, he made a formal legal request to be divorced from medicine. He called it "allopathic medicine". He also called it "old medicine".

He devised a method of care called "osteopathy", a combination of the words "osteo" for bone and "-pathy" for pathology. He saw bones as a lever or, as he put it, "the handle of a hoe", which would enhance the nervous system and, ultimately, blood flow by their manipulation/mobilization. It was his concept that the majority of the ailments were due to the inability of stagnant blood to be removed from the area of involvement. This was largely under the control of the nervous system, so removing restrictions of the nervous system was the primary goal. This could usually best be achieved by manipulation, especially of the spinal system from which all of the nerves emerged.

Because, by word of mouth, his method of care had become so successful, he could not really handle the flow of patients. Also, with the urging of the townspeople of Kirksville, Missouri, he was encouraged to open up a training center—a medical school, if you will. The people in Kirksville recognized his practice was good for business with many out-of-town patients. Of course, he did not wish to call it a medical school. It was the "American School of Osteopathy". It opened in 1892. There were seventeen people in the first class. The first class included three women. Andrew Still had no prejudice against female osteopaths and, from then on, a relatively large number of women as compared to American medical schools were accepted into the osteopatic school. Two years later, there were 200 attendees in the school of osteopathy. By 1895, due to his effective care of several politicians, it was legalized in the state of Missouri and soon many other states followed.

He was challenged by the physicians of the time as being a fake and a charlatan. They would often send normal people whom they paid to pretend to have illnesses. Consistently, Still and his trainees would pick up those who really had a problem versus a person acting as if they were sick. He was once challenged in court in Kirksville by a prominent physician, who said he was providing ineffective care. It was a jury trial in which both sides presented their cases without attorneys. Still ended his arguments by saying that he had fewer patients in the town cemetery than the doctor did. He won the case, of course, in that the fatalities secondary to manipulative care were unknown.

Against the backdrop of usually ineffective "medication" and surgery, which was often rudimentary, this very safe mechanism of care which did have a reasonable rationale often was successful. In spite of the resistance from the medical profession, it gradually grew to have various osteopathic schools around the country. Only with the emergence of evidence-based, scientific medicine was it necessary for them to modify the view that it was not necessary to treat diseases with medication or surgery. The osteopathic schools now teach a curriculum very similar to the allopathic schools.

In one of the lectures to the graduating class in 1895, Andrew Still quoted a success in treating mental disease, gynecological problems, excess fluid retention (known at that time as "dropsy") as well as sciatica, all by manipulation. The success probably was due somewhat to the lack of injury which would occur with the traditional medicine then.

Contrasted to the concepts of Kellogg and the Seventh-Day Adventist Sanitorium, there was no concern for the use of exercise. From Still's standpoint, there was a deep spiritual concept that he was merely doing "God's work" in restoring the marvelous machine of the human body to its normal state. Because of the wonderful design, the body could cure itself if given the opportunity. Osteopaths were merely the engineers, trying to steer the machinery into the correct position. Thus, in spite of totally different concepts, spiritual enthusiasm was similar to that of the Seventh-Day Adventists.

But here again, was it the idea or the personality? Certainly, with an individual who could develop a concept which was persistent and consistent, much as Robin McKenzie did, it was the personality that made it work. But charlatans come and go and, if the concept does not work, it fades with the charlatan. McKenzie care and osteopathic care persist today. Much of osteopathic care has been incorporated into mainstream medicine and, to a certain extent, the training programs between schools of osteopathy and schools of medicine have little difference. McKenzie techniques, known as mechanical diagnosis and treatment, have been identified as the most accepted concept of spinal care by American physical therapists.

While we're on the subject of manipulation, we should deal with chiropractic as well. It turns out, in the third class in 1894, an individual from Davenport, Iowa, named D. D. Palmer, took some of the training program at Still's Kirksville school. The next year, he started to practice manipulative care of the spine, which he called chiropractic. "Cheir" is Greek for the hand and "praktikos" is Greek for action. The chiropractic school was founded in 1898 in Davenport, Iowa, by Palmer.

The chiropractors, although developing concepts of benefit for health problems far in excess of back and neck pain, did not develop a need to be part of mainstream medicine. Their concept was that malalignment of the spine sent bad messages to the brain and had to be corrected by manipulation. Surgery, drugs and exercise never were part of the earlier concepts. Today, however, the influence of chiropractic, at least for spinal care, is probably as significant as that of physical therapy.

The point of this discussion, the comparison between Kellogg and Still, is to recognize the importance of the pioneer. There has to be an unwavering advocate of a concept if there is a hope for survival. Nonetheless, the survival ultimately depends upon the validity of the idea. Also, it depends upon the ability for the concept to be understood by the population at large. Although we all wish to be cured by magic, few of us can expect to "win the lottery" and we must make a positive move toward our own best interests in healthcare.

8

The Dallas Days—A Test of Personality Power

As described earlier, Proposition 13 passed in California to control property taxes. This meant the slow strangulation of financial resources for Rancho Los Amigos Hospital. I had the option of going into full-time private practice in Downey. Certainly, that would have been comfortable. I worked with a marvelous group called the Greater Los Angeles Orthopaedic Medical Group. We were financially successful and had interesting practices. On the other hand, Rancho had given me a taste of the potential to make a difference. The potential to do research, develop innovations and extend my personality beyond the one-to-one patient relationship was tantalizing. Based on my Rancho experience, I knew I was a bit ahead of the curve of traditional orthopaedics. My experience with the cast brace for femoral fractures, early fitting of below-knee amputees and the general accomplishments of early mobilization and emphasis on active treatment, which was the essence of rehabilitation as carried out at Rancho, let me know that more could be accomplished.

Although, up until that time, I had not had an academic position, the potential to make a difference seemed more likely to be in the area of academic orthopaedics than in the daily one-to-one private practice. Two other factors made the decision to make a move easy. One was the dissolution of our orthopaedic group. The web of trust of financial arrangements was destroyed when one of the partners felt he was working harder than the others and should be paid more. When the production figures became known for the first time in the history of our group, however, he was next to the bottom of financial productivity. Up to that time, we distributed the net income equally among all of the partners. The second was the apparent opportunity to take over the job as Chairman at USC, which had become open and I was led to believe that I was at the top of the list for the job.

How Do You Hedge Your Bets?

However, in order to have other options, I did look at the job in Dallas, which had been open for over a year. The previous Chairman, Dr. Gregory, had unfortunately died from a heart attack a year and a half earlier. Many people had interviewed for the job but found it unattractive. The job as Orthopaedic Professor at the University of Texas Southwestern in Dallas also meant Chief of Orthopaedics at Parkland Hospital. That phrase was attractive but the financial situation of the Orthopaedic Division in the medical school was terrible. The Division was $500,000 in debt to the Department of Surgery. There were no resources to generate clinical income. Parkland Hospital was the County Hospital, supplying care for the uninsured. Nonetheless, upon the recommendation of several senior orthopaedic academics, I was invited to interview for the job. It was a memorable experience because it was my first introduction to Texas culture.

When I arrived at the airport, I was picked up by a young member of the few remaining orthopaedic faculty members at Southwestern Medical School—Dickey Jones. That name itself resonates with Texas culture. It represented a character as other Southern names such as "Joe-Bob" and "Bubba". This guy (later we became great friends and he became a respected member of our faculty) picked me up in a huge Cadillac and he drove with one foot, wearing cowboy boots, resting on the edge of the dashboard.

I was shown around and met the current faculty, and was introduced to the dispirited residents. They had not had a chairman for a year and a half and the program seemed to have no direction. One of the senior residents, after hearing my discussion, asked, "Why in the hell would you want this damn job?" That really wasn't a great endorsement for the potential but, indeed, there were unusual potentials at this very significant and overall very well-funded university. I left from that visit with the perhaps unrealistic thought: *I know how to fix this.*

It turned out, on the last day on which the selections for the job at USC were to be made, the Dean at the University of Southern California, called me up and said, "Vert, we're sorry to lose you," which, of course, meant I didn't get the job I really wanted. I had already told the folks at Dallas that, if I didn't get the USC job, I would come. Thus, with great misgivings concerning the unknown, I moved the family to Dallas.

The two older children had finished college and were branching out on their own. However, we had a younger daughter, Mary, who was still in grade school. Naturally, we wanted to have a good school available to her and we were told that we should move to the town of Highland Park, which sits in the middle of Dallas. It turns out that Highland Park and University Park remained separate entities from the city of Dallas. Many of the professional people of Dallas lived in these two little enclaves. When Dallas was desegregated by judicial order, the judges lived in Highland Park and did not desegregate Highland Park or University Park. It remained a bastion of the Old South. We didn't know this. After we bought the house, it rapidly dawned on us what a strange place it was. But it did indeed have an excellent school system.

Off to Dallas

Actually, Dallas culturally was a total surprise.

They had just opened the Dallas-Forth Worth Airport, then the largest airport in America in terms of size, to service a metropolitan area which was the largest city not along the seacoast. It is a mercantile center. The business of Dallas is business—much of it oil business, finance and insurance. It turned out to be the most materialistic society that I have ever experienced. Everything was perception of wealth and status. This led to some strange statistics. Dallas has the largest Presbyterian Church, Methodist Church and Baptist Church in the country. On the other hand, it has the highest divorce rate and one of the highest murder rates of any metropolitan area in the country. There used to be a television show titled *Dallas,* which for several years had soap-opera-type stories of deceit and infidelity and bed-hopping. Actually, surprisingly, that series was pretty close to the truth. In the PTA book of the Highland Park school district, a phenomenon which I had never seen before was depicted. Each child, naturally, was listed in alphabetical order according to grade. After the child's name and the name of the parents, however, well over half of the children had an addendum identifying previous parents who were divorced. Some children had two previous households. Nearly all of them, however, had lived in Highland Park all of their lives.

This was a tiny enclave measuring about three-by-three miles. Yet, nearly everybody went to church on Sunday.

An interesting comment on the culture also was the problem of our young daughter, Mary, had with integrating into this new society. When she came back from her first day at school, we naturally asked the name of her teacher and she stated it to be "Miss R".

Ruth and I said, "Well, that can't be her full name. What does 'R' stand for?"

Mary insisted that was her name. We found out several weeks later, however, that the teacher's name was Ms. Orr but, due to the Dallas accent falling upon Mary's California ears, that's the way it sounded. Because of her difficulty understanding the dialect, we had a teacher's conference where she was being prepared to be sent to the dyslexic class organized for the mentally disabled. Of course, Mary was quite normal and the whole problem was her inability to get the words in "Texan". The problem settled down but the teachers in Highland Park always considered Mary's mental deficiency without any regard to whether there was any fault with communication. The people in the "Republic of Texas" tend to be pretty secure that they have it right!

From my wife's standpoint, the culture was very strange. People would typically tell her, "Y'all come back, y'hear." She rapidly learned that that did not really mean come back. They never wanted to see you again. That's just what people said. Nobody asked us to their house as a neighbor for ten years. Of course, there were many parties but these were all based on professional relationships. Finding friendly neighbors was extremely difficult. Ruth never was comfortable with a society which was so materialistic and so superficial. When we moved back to California eleven years later and were searching for new furniture, we were passing one of the discount stores, called Fed-Mart. That was one of the stores where you buy a membership and have a card which allows you discounts. I turned to Ruth and said, "I'm sorry we don't have our old Fed-Mart card." She turned to me and pulled out her wallet and took out the Fed-Mart card, which she had kept alive for twelve years. She calmly said, "We've got it." She always knew we'd be back.

But the professional life was marvelous. It was just the opportunity I wanted. There was plenty of clinical material. There were a group of eager trainees (orthopaedic residents) and the opportunity to try almost anything. I did have to learn new skills, however.

Contrasted to Rancho Los Amigos Hospital, where, if you had a good idea, you merely had to organize a plan and there were always funds and staff who could carry it out, in the academic world of any medical school or any university, it is a constant turf battle. There are a finite amount of funds available. You find yourself competing with other departments for a piece of the pie. It took unusual political skills of horse trading to get what you wanted. It was a true political game, just as exists in any legislature. You give to get.

We were a division of the Department of Surgery, who controlled our funds. What eventually led to my departure after eleven years was the inability for orthopaedics to gain the status of an independent department. By that time, we had erased the $500,000 deficit and, by clinical activity, had come to have a $500,000 positive balance. A significant amount of our funds, however, were being skimmed off by the Department of Surgery. These funds could have been used by orthopaedics for continued research but we were stunted in our abilities. Thus, I submitted my letter of resignation with the reason that, if we could not be made a department, I would leave. It was accepted. However, as they searched for a new chairman when I left in 1988, the turmoil and unveiling of the financial rigging were of such a spectacular nature that, when the dust finally settled, the Dean was gone, the Chairman of General Surgery was gone, we did get to be a department and the number-two man in the previous division of Orthopaedic Surgery, Dr. Bucholtz, was the new Chairman of the Orthopaedic Department. He eventually became president of the National Society, the American Academy of Orthopaedic Surgeons.

But the eleven years were very exciting. Parkland was one of the largest trauma centers in the country. We developed many techniques in the care of trauma which are currently used today. When I arrived in 1977, the average time a patient with a closed femoral fracture would be in the hospital was six weeks. When I left, it was four days, thanks to the development of surgical techniques, early mobilization, etc. This was not just our work, but the whole field of Orthopaedic Surgery was developing a wide array of surgical solutions.

Starting Spinal Surgery

In addition, because I had experience with private practice in Downey, I was able to develop a system of private practice in Dallas in association with various doctors in the community. There was a hospital a half a block away from Parkland Hospital, called Medical Arts, where a surgical practice in spine care was being carried out. I joined with Dr. David Selby and we worked together doing spinal fusions on patients with painful discs. Thanks to a very excellent surgeon, Dr. Robert Henderson, we became experts with anterior surgery (surgery of the spine through the abdomen) and developed a significant success rate. Great emphasis was placed on picking patients with appropriate

141

pathology and emotional status on which we could do surgery. Numerous papers were published and our success rate among others changed many aspects of surgical care for the degenerating spine. As we'll see later, that was not all to the good.

Because of that experience, I became involved with the early development of two professional organizations involved with spine care. The first was the International Society for the Study of Lumbar Spine. In 1986, I became president and we had an international conference in Dallas. I was also involved with the formation of the North American Spine Society and became president in 1988. These were the beginnings of the swing toward surgical care of the spine, which has continued to grow. More and more types of implants have been developed and, most recently, a total disc replacement has been developed. There are significant problems, however. Much of the care in spinal surgery is in the treatment of pain. Fractures, tumors or neurologic disability are a small part of the problem and treated well with surgery. But it is often difficult to solve a pain problem by surgical care. This had not quite dawned on me at the time I was in Dallas. I didn't also appreciate the significant financial aspects related to this. The implants became more and more costly but the commercial involvement of manufacturers became more widespread. More and more money was involved with spinal care. To a certain extent, that clouded the perception of what really needed to be done.

While the spine surgery practice took up a small part of my professional life, the majority of work was related to the educational program for the residents and medical students at the University. This was really fun. Because I was a bit of a maverick and had some unconventional ideas, it made for great conferences with a lot of discussion. Of course, that's the essence of a learning experience. Socrates knew that. The fun of working with young people, each with strong egos, strong personalities and an enthusiasm for work, was really exciting. It is truly hard work to be an orthopaedic resident. There are many hours on call, a lot of frustration, many things that don't work as well as you wish. It takes an unusual personality to tolerate all this. But they were also eager learners.

How Do You Pick the Right Trainee?

That brings us to the selection process of residents. We had, with our resources, a very excellent training program. We always had a large number of applicants for the five positions a year as an orthopedic resident at Parkland and the University of Texas Southwestern. We would cull the number of applicants down (from over a hundred) to a manageable number to interview—say, about thirty—and then try to rank them as to most appropriate. Of course, the residents would be applying to other programs as well. I early learned, however, that sometimes how an applicant appeared on paper with all their achievements and background did not fully define their potential. Therefore, early in my tenure as Chairman, I initiated the rule that the committee could pick four out of the five but I would have an opportunity to pick one of the applicants based purely on my gut feeling of their potential. That worked out very well. Usually they did not have the best grades or best record of achievement with various scholastic or community service, etc. In the interview process, however, I found I just "liked them". I must say that every one of these gut selections turned out to be marvelous clinicians and effective orthopaedic surgeons.

On the other hand, some of those with the highest grades and the most significant recommendations had their flaws. There was an occasion when one of the residents, who had the highest grades from high school as well as medical school and even had played on his college football team, emerged as an intern at Parkland. All of our residents had to serve a year working at Parkland as interns. There was an occasion when he was supposed to hang up an IV bottle to provide some fluid to a patient in the Emergency Room and, although he said he did it, he didn't do it. On the basis of that event, I fired him.

On the other hand, in that he came from a very wealthy family and had many family members who were attorneys, there was a problem. He pointed out that there were no previous warnings to him concerning this behavior. He told me I did not have a leg to stand on. I conferred with the attorneys at the University and they agreed. Thus, against my better judgement, I had him working in the lab for a year while he "matured". Indeed, that's exactly what he did and he turned out to be a fine orthopaedic surgeon, practicing in the community now. Years later, at a cocktail party, his wife came up to me and said the best thing that ever happened to him was when I fired him. The point is, it's awfully hard to pick the right person based on past record, past letters of recommendations and academic achievement. What really makes a person function is difficult to discern until you see them in action.

A False Start in Rehabilitation

One of the projects I wished to implement when I took over the job as Orthopaedic Chairman at UT Southwestern was to develop an active rehabilitation system much as had been accomplished at Rancho Los Amigos Hospital. There was a small facility only about half a mile away from the medical school in Parkland. I arranged to get on the Board of Directors and found that they were searching for a new Medical Director. The facility had been functioning as a nursing home/rest home in the past.

A previous Rancho graduate with whom I had worked when he was a resident there and I knew to be interested in such an opportunity. I approached George Wharton, who was then working in Jackson, Mississippi, and it was the right time for him. He did come to Dallas and started an active rehabilitation program, somewhat in the image of Rancho Los Amigos. It took on the project of treating spinal cord injuries, head injuries, strokes, etc. It was renamed the "Dallas Rehab Institute".

That was the first step of the plan. The second step was to route residents through that program so that they could get an understanding of the potentials of active rehabilitation techniques. They would be able to see intelligent and resourceful allied health personnel in the professions of physical therapy, occupational therapy and orthotics and prosthetics at work. This would be a marvelous educational experience, just like it had been for me and even George Wharton in the days at Rancho. That was far from the reality.

The residents hated the rotation. There was very little surgery to be done. They found themselves subservient to the allied health people—reasonably because those folks did know more about the problem being treated than the orthopedic resident. Each one of them hated the rotation more than the ones before them. They wrote letters, had committee meetings, had delegations to the faculty, etc. Finally, we scrapped the whole idea. The chemistry just wasn't there. Perhaps the volume of patients was not large enough. Perhaps the charismatic leadership wasn't there. Perhaps orthopaedics had changed so much to be a surgical specialty that digression into nonoperative care was considered wasteful in their training time. Sadly, I never could get the residents interested in any aspect of rehabilitation.

The rehabilitation aspects of orthopaedics were becoming a smaller and smaller area of interest from the specialty as a whole. Far better surgical care for fractures had developed. The age of total joint replacements was just emerging. Arthroscopy (the visualization of a joint by placing small tubes into the joint) was just beginning to develop. My enthusiasm for rehabilitation was beginning to leave me, as I became more involved in the mainstream of orthopaedics.

A New Insight—Exercise Physiology

And then another unguarded moment occurred. About the time I left Los Angeles, one of the primary care doctors we knew in Downey said that a house was for sale next to his in South Lake Tahoe. This was right on the Keys, which was a very nicely arranged inland waterway with all of the houses on the water with a dock. I went into partnership with Vernon Nickel and we bought the place. I envisioned it as a gathering place for what was going to be a scattered family with the older kids going their way around the country. Indeed, it worked out very well, and we held onto the house for twenty-five years. A lot of happy vacations were spent there, sailing in the summer and skiing in the winter.

But the occasion for new insight occurred unexpectedly. It turns out that an orthopaedic surgeon named Richard Steadman was practicing in South Lake Tahoe. Actually, I met him almost accidentally while we picked up a tennis game together. He lived a few blocks from our house. He already had a certain degree of fame in the sports medicine world because of his skill in returning injured world-class skiers to their previous high levels of performance. This was unexpected. A complex ankle fracture had doomed an expert skier in the past. Many of these skiers had suffered significant lower extremity fractures, which he was able to put together with the much better screws, plates, pins and rods. A system for surgical care developed largely in Switzerland and Germany had been taken over by American surgeons now, which allowed rather precise reconstruction of even significant joint injuries.

What was different about Dick Steadman was his method of rehabilitation. He did not send them to the usual physical therapy. He worked with an exercise physiologist to carry out an array of progressive exercises using bicycles, free weights and various forms of equipment. Until I became aware of this system of rehabilitation, I didn't even know what an exercise physiologist was. Many of these athletes stayed at local hotels or even at Steadman's house while they were going through their postsurgical training phase. As a result of these exercises, they regained full range of motion in their joints—usually the ankle but also the knee—and returned to the full strength required to carry out their very high level sports performance. Soon, athletes from other sports than skiing emerged to be cared for by Steadman. His fame grew and he eventually left South Lake Tahoe and moved to Vail, Colorado, to develop a world-famous clinic.

What was impressive, however, was that he got the best out of his surgical reconstruction with an active, progressive exercise program carried out along physiologic principles of muscle strengthening, tissue training and aerobic exercises. That was my first insight into the value of active rehabilitation programs for people with more common musculoskeletal disability than spinal cord injuries, head trauma and strokes.

It is hard to believe now but, at that time, in the late 1970s and the 1980s, these ideas were somewhat revolutionary. Even the idea of aerobic exercise was controversial. It turns out that the innovator of the concept—graded cardiovascular challenging exercises known as aerobic exercises—had developed a rehab center, only about a mile from the medical school. That was Dr. Kenneth Cooper.

While Dr. Cooper was a military doctor with the Air Force, trying to develop some standardization of fitness, he developed a system of grading cardiovascular fitness on the basis of pulse rate, oxygen consumption and respiratory rate. This developed into a point system and the whole concept was called aerobics. In South America, the points are called "Coopers" in honor of their developer. When I arrived at Dallas, I was aware of Dr. Cooper's achievements and thought I would like to be involved with his research. I was somewhat surprised to find that he had no connection with the medical school in spite of, even at that time, a worldwide reputation. He had written several books on the subject and had popularized the whole idea of jogging for health.

When I approached the chairman of the Department of Internal Medicine concerning an invitation to have Dr. Cooper work with us in orthopaedics relative to some exercise programs, he was aghast. He pointed out that Dr. Cooper did not have his boards in internal medicine and had never held any academic position. Lacking the appropriate credentials, it would be quite unseemly to have Dr. Cooper associated with the faculty. Amazing! Here he was, changing the whole attitude of the public toward fitness and its role in prevention of later cardiac problems, high blood pressure and obesity, and the academic department felt he was insufficiently credentialed!

I visited Dr. Cooper several times and found him to be a zealot and an enthusiast for the concepts he had developed. On the other hand, at that time, he had no interest in the role of progressive resistance exercises and their impact on health. At that time, neither did I.

The Growth of Sports Medicine

A word about sports medicine. Richard Steadman was a pioneer in this field. What made it different from orthopaedics in general? Really, nothing. It was just skilled surgical care applied to athletes. What created the field of sports medicine was television. Once sports became broadcast on television, people could often see the action up close, more than they could if they were watching it at the arena. They might even see a traumatic event occur. Then, a few months later, that injured athlete would reappear, hopefully performing at a level near his or her proficiency before the injury event. The efficacy of treatment could be graded somewhat by whether or not the athlete ever did return to his or her usual performance. There was an effective measurement of effective care, given a specific diagnosis.

More than the observation of injury to the athlete, the value of the athlete and the speed of his return became important features of the business of professional athletics. Television brought in the dollars which made million-dollar athletes commonplace. When the very expensive athlete was injured and unavailable for the rest of the season, someone was losing a lot of money. Thus, how fast the injury could be rehabilitated to allow the athlete to return became not only a medical care matter but a financial matter. To a certain extent, the doctors became graded on their ability to do just that—return the athlete to usual performance as fast as possible. That's what made Richard Steadman so successful. In the world of public interest, it's more important how fast the skier got back to topflight performance compared to how fast grandma recovered from her fractured hip. In one sense, measurement of the patient's performance became an area of heightened interest thanks to television and sports medicine.

Orthopaedic sports medicine was a blossoming area of orthopaedic practice and, as such, became a new source of clinical income. Also at this time in the 1970s and 1980s, a new form of training was developed. One could become a specialist by taking a residency program but, to become skilled in the developing new areas, such as sports medicine, an additional apprenticeship was necessary. These were identified as fellowships.

When I recognized what was going on with Dick Steadman, I encouraged him to accept one of our graduating residents as an apprentice—a fellow—for six months. He could even stay at our house in Lake Tahoe during this period of time. It worked out nicely and, for the next several years, one of our residents would rotate through the Steadman clinic to develop the skills of a sports medicine orthopaedic surgeon.

But in Dallas, at the medical school, we could never develop a system of rehabilitation based on principles of progressive physical training such as Steadman had at Tahoe. Orthopaedics did not control physical therapy.

Orthotics and Prosthetics

There was one area of rehabilitation which I was able to transfer from my Rancho experience into Texas. Shortly after I showed up in Dallas, there was a reception at which I was being introduced as the new chairman of orthopaedics. On that occasion, I met the president of the University of

Texas Southwestern. He was a retired internal medicine doctor who was in charge of the entire medical center—not just the medical school, which was directed by the dean. As we had our casual conversation, he indicated that he had a problem. The state legislature had recently directed him to have a podiatry school. The podiatrists were trying to achieve status at a level of the medical doctors. The medical doctors were resisting this with the justification that an M.D. educational program was far more extensive and comprehensive than that of a podiatrist, who only took care of the feet. The podiatrist's point of view was that, because their training was more focused, they were better at dealing with the feet than anyone else, including the surgery.

Of course, there was a matter of turf in that certainly the orthopaedic surgeons did not enjoy another specialty taking over surgical care of the feet. Recognizing all these factors, the president, Charley Sprague, didn't want to start the political firestorm which would occur if a podiatry school were on the campus of the medical school. In that the professional schools were state supported, the podiatrists had a reasonable case that they deserved a school in Texas as well. Because orthopaedics was the specialty that would be most affected by a podiatric invasion, he asked if I had any advice. In another one of those unguarded moments, it struck me that nowhere in Texas was there a training program for prosthetists, the people who make artificial limbs, and orthotists, the brace makers. So, I said, "Why not have a prosthetic/orthotic school?"

He said, with honest naïveté, 'What do they do?"

Once I explained, he looked quite pleased. He said, "That sounds similar: podiatrist, prosthetist. I think I can sell that to the legislature." He did. That's how things get done in Texas!

So, we started an orthotic/prosthetic program and it still continues. Based on that program, we put on training programs for residents from many programs for the next ten years. We also produced a series of technicians who carried out the work of making artificial limbs and assistive devices.

The orthotic/prosthetic school allowed us to carry out additional testing of various materials which could be used with the supportive devices being constructed. Most of the interest in orthopaedics at that time was in implants to stabilize fractures and to create artificial joints. There was little interest in external support systems, but research funding was therefore a little easier to get. We were able to get some grants and developed a research lab at the Dallas Veterans Hospital. That lab would later supply the technicians to do electrical testing of muscle function, especially in the back.

That testing lab at the VA also brought me to interface with a fascinating young plastic surgeon—Dr. Ralph Holmes. He had finished his residency program with the plastic surgery division at the medical school and had been assigned to direct plastic surgery at the Dallas VA. It turns out that facial reconstruction is a phase of plastic surgery which is seldom talked about in today's Plastic Surgery world seen in the advertising for liposuction, breast augmentation or reduction, tummy tuck, etc. Secondary to disease or injury, on some occasions the bones of the face are destroyed and thus the usual facial contours cannot be maintained. In other areas of the body, transplanted bone, known as bone grafting, works quite nicely. Usually one can take some bone from areas of the pelvis, where it really isn't needed, and transfer it to areas where there are bony defects such as bone loss from infection or dead bone created by trauma.

Ralph Holmes and Coral

Bone grafting to the facial bones, however, is very unpredictable. Sometimes the plastic surgeon would replace a lower jaw segment, lost perhaps to tumor, but would find out, much to everyone's displeasure, that the graft would melt away. It seemed to be totally unpredictable.

A few years earlier, a physician at Penn State University had noticed the similarity between various forms of coral to human bone. Human bone comes essentially in two forms, the first is known as cortical bone, which is the compact bone which makes our tubular bones. Also, in the wide spaces of bones, a lattice form of bone, known as cancellous bone, is prominent. This bone has multiple interconnecting channels which actually supply the foundation for production of blood cells.

Cancellous bone is not as strong as cortical bone but it is resilient and can stand significant forces without cracking. A certain type of coral known as genus porites looks like cortical bone and genus goniapora looks like cancellous bone. The coral is calcium carbonate, which also has some natural impurities. It was constructed in the ocean by tiny organisms over years. If implanted in the body, there may be some reaction to this foreign material. However, in the Penn State labs, they had discovered a method called "replamiformation" which, in an environment of heat and vacuum, converted the calcium carbonate mineral to a different crystalline structure known as calcium hydroxyapatite. This is the exact crystal which makes up human bones. The process also purified the material so that there were no other foreign materials. The coral could be implanted in human tissues and there was no foreign body reaction. It was rapidly incorporated. The immune system didn't notice it.

At the time I met Ralph Holmes, he was reconstructing surgically created defects in jaws of dogs with the Penn State coral. I saw the histology in the microscopic slides. This showed excellent incorporation of the coral into the host mandible of the dog. I was familiar with this type of histology because, back when we were trying to develop a skeletal implant for a limb prosthesis fixation, we were using ceramics (coral is also a type of ceramic) with various sized holes drilled in them and knew the limits of incorporation if there were no interconnecting channels or the diameter of the holes too small.

Based on my very favorable impression of the whole procedure, I turned over to Ralph the majority of the research funding which had been provided to me by the University upon my taking the job as Chairman. He had the most innovative research. In order to quantitate the amount of host bone ingrowth into the implant material, he also developed a system of reflection electron microscopy with accompanying computerized measurement of void space, native bone and coral. This was all pretty dramatic stuff and certainly new. We produced several papers in that regard. For the first time, the amount of bone ingrowth into a foreign material could be quantified.

Later on, we converted the animal work into human work and started using the coral for bone substitutes in areas where there had been loss due to crushing of cancellous bone secondary to fracture. By this time, the system had been commercialized and a company called Interpore was marketing the material. Indeed, it was very successful and is used today as a bone substitute to fill voids in wrist fractures and in fractures around the knee. Thus, it is unnecessary to get bone graft from the pelvis.

Actually, Ralph Holmes was a native of San Diego and, after about five years at the VA in Dallas, an opportunity emerged in the Plastic Surgery Department at University of California San Diego and he moved his work there. He continued and expanded it into other materials. Along with other scientists, he developed a biodegradable plastic called "MacroPore", which does an even better job for facial and dental reconstruction as well as some areas of orthopedics. His research led down a different road than seemed to parallel my interests.

However, the most important unguarded moment of my time in Dallas occurred about the time that Ralph left. It was the occasion of a phone call from a former resident at Rancho Los Amigos, Dr. Tom Mayer. He had been a resident on the Problem Back Service at Rancho Los Amigos Hospital. He had been a resident from the UC San Francisco program. He was one of the few residents who really got enthusiastic about the Problem Back Service and, indeed, when he returned to his home program in San Francisco, tried to get the staff to develop a rehabilitation system somewhat like what was going on at Rancho. No success there.

The Impact of Tom Mayer

Tom became interested in the emerging area of sports medicine, but he saw it more focused on the weekend athlete. When he finished his training program, he made his decision as to where to practice based on the educational levels of the potential clientele. It turns out that Los Alamos, New Mexico, famous or infamous because the location of the atomic bomb labs, was his choice. Actually, apparently the city has the highest percentage of Ph.D.s of any city in the country. He moved there with his wife, Holly, and their two children, after a two-year "sabbatical" following graduation from the residency program. He, Holly and the kids decided to tour the world, working part-time at various governmental agencies to supply medical help and gain some funding for the next leg of their trip. Holly was a very well-trained nurse and he was a fully trained orthopaedic surgeon. They did offer a very useful addition, at least briefly, to many treatment programs around the world. That little anecdote gives a depiction of Tom's maverick nature.

But back to the phone call. It turns out that, after a few years in practice, he had developed some sort of allergic optic neuritis. His central vision had been destroyed. He could only see vaguely at the periphery. He certainly no longer could do surgery. He could not even drive a car and he had to read with magnification. This was a devastating blow to this very talented and energetic young Orthopaedic surgeon. He had been an expert skier and outdoorsman.

What he called me about was an inquiry as to whether there was a possible position on our faculty at Dallas. From my standpoint, I thought this was a great opportunity. To find a young, energetic, well-trained Orthopaedic surgeon who, unfortunately, could no longer do surgery supplied just the resource I needed. He recognized that one of the few things he could do was to direct rehabilitation.

As mentioned earlier, trying to develop a viable rehab program similar to Rancho Los Amigos Hospital so far had been a complete flop in Dallas. Perhaps Tom, with his experience and skills, could revitalize the project. I thus found a way to put him on our part-time faculty with some financial support. He was assigned to the Dallas Rehabilitation Institute and developed a pain program focused at chronic back problems.

This was a time when the phenomenon known as "pain clinics" was emerging as an adjunct to chronic care programs. The pain clinics routinely had psychologists involved and a whole array of psychological treatment systems, such as biofeedback, cognitive therapy, group sessions and, especially, psychological testing. The need to measure mental status was becoming accepted. More important, that acceptance meant reimbursement by insurance companies. It was emerging that people in chronic pain, especially back pain, often had significant psychological burdens, some preexistent, some following the onset of their back problems. The coupling of a physical treatment program with a psychological treatment program, of course, made the ideal model for treatment of chronic disorders with disability secondary to both pain and mechanical dysfunction such as chronic back pain.

Because Tom Mayer now was involved in this sort of work, he went to various meetings where chronic pain management was the center of discussion. He was probably the only orthopaedic surgeon there, as most clinicians were in the psychological world.

As was planned, he started to develop a program at the Dallas Rehab Institute shortly after he arrived in Dallas in October of 1981. There gradually grew personality clashes with various people working at Dallas Rehab and some of the psychologists already working with the spine surgeons. They saw Tom as a threat to their positions in that, because he was going to various meetings related to chronic pain and chronic back problems, he began to get a handle on what was really going on. He began to know much more about the psychology of chronic pain than most Orthopaedic surgeons and even many psychologists.

The First Spine Testing Equipment

About this time, in the early eighties, a very energetic Orthopaedic surgeon from San Antonio, Walt Simmons, began putting on annual conferences concerning the complex problem of chronic back pain. These were known as "The Challenge of the Lumbar Spine". They were directed at all of the various players in the complex treatment problem of chronic back pain. He was always searching for innovations and new ways to solve the poorly understood problems of chronic back pain. He also was quite an entrepreneur and had many connections in the business world. And, as a past military physician, he was aware of fitness and the need for therapeutic exercise. Also, he did have a rehabilitation center in San Antonio with some exercise equipment.

At that time, the major measurement tool in an active exercise program was the Cybex equipment, which used the isokinetic system. This system controlled the rate of motion but measured force. Thus, patterns of performance could be depicted, noting average torque, maximum torque, etc. It all could be digested by the computer and one could come up with a numeric description of joint performance as well as a graphic depiction. This had been quite successful for the knee rehabilitation so the manufacturers, recognizing the large potential market in back pain, had just developed a piece of equipment designed for the spine. The first one had been supplied to two sports medicine physical therapists in Wisconsin. Because their clientele really did not have back pain, they did nothing with it. The second had been supplied to Walt Simmons and, because of Tom's association with Walt, he contacted the company concerning the possibility that he might have one of these tools.

The Cybex Company, of course, needed credibility for the equipment and Tom's association with the medical school as an Assistant Professor gave the credibility needed. It turned out that the Physical Therapy Department at University of Texas Southwestern also had some extra space and were pleased to have a new piece of equipment donated.

Thus, in the late summer of 1982, the back testing equipment showed up in Dallas, and this started the use of exercise equipment for testing and treating the back.

As in all of medicine, the key to understanding the effect of treatment is to clarify the dose and note the response. That's a pretty easy project when dealing with pharmaceuticals. A defined amount of antibiotic will cause a decrease in temperature and resolution of the infection. For musculoskeletal problems, the dose of treatment in the form of exercise is not too complex when dealing with the extremities. The performance of the uninjured extremity is available for testing. Thus, it can be compared to the injured joint. In the spine, however, lacking something to compare to, measurement for deviation from normal is difficult. But one cannot identify dose response unless it is apparent how far from normal the individual being treated presents himself. Thus, the first stage in the use of the Cybex equipment was to establish normal levels of function of the lumbar spine, both in strength and range. This had to be done for various age groups and the genders, for later comparison to patients with back pain. This work was published in 1984. With that background, one could now start testing patients.

A space had opened up next to the Cybex unit in the physical therapy facility and Tom happily moved his program from the Dallas Rehab Institute. This was at the off-campus site used by the university physical therapists, which was designed for them to carry out a clinical practice. He called the new rehab center, PRIDE (Productive Rehabilitation Institute of Dallas for Ergonomics). It was in May of 1983. With the background of measurement of normals, it now became clear that the weakness in people with chronic back pain was not in the abdominal muscles but was in the lumbar extensor muscles. The ratio of strength between the two could be used as a predictor of severity of the back problem. Actually, that was news. Up until then, it had been accepted that back pain was associated with weak abdominals, flexors of the spine or even problems with muscle strength.

As had been recognized earlier, there was a psychological component involved with chronic back pain and, thanks to some connections in the medical school, Tom was able to attract a young psychologist researcher, Robert Gatchel, to join him to start a new, innovative rehabilitation program. Also, in that the majority of the patient's had their onset secondary to workplace injuries and their insurance coverage was workers' compensation insurance, return to work was an important goal to maintain persistent referrals from the Texas workers compensation system. Thus, he hired an occupational therapist, Nancy Kishino. This was an innovative mix of skills in a pain clinic—an orthopaedic surgeon, a university psychologist and a well-trained occupational therapist in addition to an expert physical therapist in this situation—Sue Smith.

They began processing patients with a combination of measurement of function, gradual progressive exercise programs, psychological testing and treatment. All of the programs were focused on returning to the workplace. It was totally unique at the time. Their work was eventually recognized in 1984 by receiving the Volvo Award at the Annual Meeting of the International Society for the Study of the Lumbar Spine. That award was for the most significant research worldwide. This study depicted the superior results of treatment by the specialized techniques described above. The dose response was clarified by both physical testing and psychological testing. There was excellent follow-up of the graduates of the program at a level of ninety-five percent, which is nearly unknown in clinical studies in America. The results of those who had completed the study were compared to those with those who had been turned down by their insurance companies and were treated in other ways. In that group, forty-one percent had returned to work whereas, in the treatment group, eighty-seven percent had returned to work. In the usual treatment group, there were five times more doctor visits during the two-year follow-up period compared to those in the PRIDE treated group. There were few surgeries in the treatment group and twice as many surgeries in the non-treatment group. The study demonstrated a dramatic change in spine care. It documented that a guided, measured exercise program was far more effective than usual care.

The study was later published in the *Journal of the American Medical Association* in 1987.

Trying to Change the World with Facts

But it wasn't easy. Even in academic circles, there are intrigues and politics. It turns out that, once the paper had been submitted to the International Society for Study of the Lumbar Spine for the next meeting, there were problems. One of the prominent orthopaedic surgeons doing spine care in Dallas met the Chairman of the Evaluation Committee for the Volvo Award, Dr. Alf Nachemson. The Volvo award is given each year for the best research in lumbar spine evaluation and treatment. Having worked with Tom, but jealous of his success, this doctor indicated to Alf that the raw data making up the impressive statistics had been "adjusted", and that their follow-up had not been as extensive as depicted. On the basis of this conversation, Dr. Nachemson contacted me. The study came from my academic division. He expressed concern about the validity of the study, indicating that it would not be accepted unless the veracity of the follow-up data was confirmed by an independent source. I therefore convened an academic committee with three knowledgeable but uninvolved researchers (whose time I had to pay for out of my divisional funds) to review the data and call patients randomly to ascertain that they had really been contacted and their follow-up information was correct. It took several months. It was somewhat like a recount of a close election. However, the report at the end of the review confirmed exactly the data that had been submitted by Tom Mayer and his associates. I had been included in the original manuscripts as a coauthor because of my financial and institutional support for the whole project. We were all pleased how it turned out. It was presented on schedule.

The experience did confirm how difficult it is to be a pioneer. The work described by Tom and his associates went against then accepted "reality". It was assumed that, after spine fusions, one could never go back to work. For instance, one of the local surgeons in Dallas had instructed one of the patients whom I saw later to never lift anything heavier than a beer can. It was assumed that motion to the injured back was a bad thing. Purposely instructing patients to improve their range of motion as well as strength was considered heresy. To train the lumbar extensors rather than the lumbar flexors was thought to be justified. Even though the experimental evidence showed the extensors were weaker, "everybody" knew that abdominal strengthening was the right method to achieve success in treating back problems. It took years for the concept of gradual progressive physical training to be accepted as a reasonable treatment program for chronic back and neck problems. Even today, the concept is generally poorly accepted when compared to other modalities of physical therapy such as massage and manipulation and electrical stimulation.

Slowly, the purpose of this whole adventure story is emerging. The demonstration that a more evidence-based idea had difficulty being accepted when it contrasts with the accepted traditions too severely is the point. It took me years to understand this, as will be further described in this meandering tale of discovery. Learning is a difficult task when so few others accept the reality.

9

Back to California, Discovery and Disappointment

As was described earlier, I took the job in Dallas as a second choice due to my failure to be selected as Chairman at USC. As many aspects of life teach us, security and progress seldom coexist. Based on my many political connections in Southern California, I felt the job at USC was secure. It was not. It was taken by a colleague to whom I had mentioned the significant amount of research funding available at USC. When I showed up at Dallas, I had no previous experience in academic medicine and was not adept at the politics. Thus, I was more or less flimflammed by the crafty chairmen of the other surgical specialties, especially the Chairman of General Surgery. I had been told to secure a position as Chairman of a department but, lacking experience, I did not fully recognize the implications and the importance of that. Unhappily, we did not control the majority of our funds and thus our academic destiny was in the hands of others. This led to the letter of resignation in 1987, which indicated that either I become a Department Head or I would resign six months later. Six months later, nothing had happened and thus it was appropriate that I leave Dallas.

Although the new Chairman situation was still in limbo and would not be decided for another year and a half, the faculty and financial situation were quite stable. We had excellent residents and the training program was progressing marvelously well. I felt no regrets as I left that I was leaving the program in the lurch. It was in excellent hands.

On the other hand, what was I to do? As this adventure being described in these chapters unfolds, once again an unguarded moment occurred.

The Corporate Hospital Business

This was the time of hospital corporations emerging. Large business organizations with wealthy investors were buying up hospitals and converting the system into profitable businesses. Up until this time, hospitals were largely developed locally. They were often branches of a church organization and thus the names of many of the hospitals we recognize today: Mount Sinai, Presbyterian, St. Francis, etc. Due to their religious or community heritage, they seldom could be characterized as sound businesses. On the other hand, the economics of the medical business was changing radically. Health insurance was part of the pay package of most employments. Medicare had passed, which guaranteed reimbursement for the older age group. Actually, for the first time, there was big money to be made in medicine. Thus, there was enthusiasm in the business community to get part of the action.

One of these businesses—Hospital Corporation of America—saw an opportunity in Southern California to develop a hospital which would be associated with the young University of California at Irvine. At that time, UCI was the youngest of the medical schools set up in California under the State University system. The oldest was in San Francisco, the second oldest at UCLA. Next in maturity was UC San Diego and then, finally, UC Irvine, which was actually an outgrowth of the California College of Osteopathic Medicine in the 1950s. The town of Irvine was an emerging suburbia, which had not yet fallen to the bedevilment of urban sprawl because the land had been controlled for many years by a single family. The founding family had bought the rights to the land extending from the mountains to the sea from the original family, who had been awarded this tract of land at the time California took over the original Spanish Grant lands. For many years, it was a land protected for its agricultural purposes and thus relatively pristine. Finally, the controlling family sold the land to a consortium, which planned to develop a controlled community. This, of course, would make an excellent college town and, with significant political give and take, in the 1960s, the University of California at Irvine was established and a major campus was built.

The medical training resource, as was the event in so many cases, such as University of Texas Southwestern and University of California at San Francisco, was the original county hospital of that area. Orange County Hospital became the teaching hospital of UCI. This excellent training program, however, had the burdens of any county hospital. The people being treated generally were the medically indigent. They had poor financial resources, if insurance at all. This was no place to develop a successful clinical practice for the medical faculty, even for a wealthy university such as the University of California.

Thus, it was easy for the Hospital Corporation of America to make a pitch to the Dean at UCI to build another hospital in the town of Irvine and call it the Irvine Medical Center. It would be at the confluence of two major freeways and in the midst of an emerging industrial park. The economic success of such a hospital would seem to be guaranteed. UCI agreed to the proposition.

166

It was then that the group in charge of this development turned to me. Someone had become aware that I had resigned from the position in Dallas and therefore was available to move. They contacted me and asked what would be the most appropriate mechanism to create a successful orthopaedic program in the hospital. Orthopaedics and cardiac surgery make the most money for hospitals. The answer to that question was easy and quick. As has been pointed out in many instances earlier in this discussion, musculoskeletal disease had few opportunities for measurement. On the other hand, there is no question that, ultimately, reimbursement would be based on demonstration of effective care. If the hospital could include systems which would measure musculoskeletal function, it would become a center of orthopaedic care. Certainly that was true in the world of cardiac surgery, where the various marvelous radiographic and electronic systems to monitor cardiac function had clearly identified appropriate candidates for cardiac surgery and were beginning to guide the rehabilitation program.

Thus, from the businessman's standpoint, this seemed to be an easy concept to grasp. It made sense—if you could document benefit of care, providers would happily reimburse you and patients would be pleased to show up at the best place there was. As history indicates, that was a very naïve concept but it certainly made sense. Thus, as an inducement to come to UCI, they offered me a $500,000 budget to establish just such a program as I had envisioned.

Also, fortunately, the Dean at UCI Medical School at that time had a son-in-law who was an orthopaedic surgeon. The Chairman of Orthopaedics at UCI actually was one of my previous partners in practice at the Greater Los Angeles Orthopaedic Medical Group—Dr. Mark Hoffer. It would be a politically friendly environment. I readily agreed to the

167

concept. As I left Dallas, the hospital in Irvine was being built.

There was the proposition of how to create an evaluation and training center. I needed help there. I really didn't know enough about equipment and the specifics of physical therapy. While in Dallas, I had met an entrepreneurial therapist—Gary Jarvis—and together we crafted a budget proposal for the specific equipment. At that time, the most accepted measurement systems for musculoskeletal problems were the isokinetic systems of Cybex. Also, they manufactured various pieces of exercise equipment. Thus, we submitted a budget to purchase a large amount of equipment and establish an evaluation and treatment center, which we called "The PAR Center" (Physical Assessment and Rehabilitation Center). The name seemed to fit. After all, par was a measure of success in physical achievement. Due to the rules of golf, in contrast to nearly every other sport for keeping score, the lower number of par was the more successful achievement. Nonetheless, the implication was quite appropriate. Progress should be measured. The Center was opened shortly after I arrived in 1988.

Then came the shock. I discovered that physical therapists did not want to measure progress or anything. With their pleasure in hands-on care, the subjective statement by the treated patient was considered adequate to define success. Even though we had invested a considerable amount of money in test equipment, they never used it. Indeed, insurance reimbursed the Center for testing. We could make money on testing. They didn't choose to use the equipment. I was astounded. We hired an athletic trainer, whose total job was to do the testing on the exercise equipment in terms of range of motion, strength, peak torque and average torque on the isokinetic equipment, and test retest status. That was the most difficult thing to achieve. There was not much resistance to having a baseline test of function, but the therapists very much resisted a follow-up test using the same mechanism of evaluation to clarify progress in an objective manner.

This was startling. The core of scientific medicine is objective definition of progress. In the orthopaedic world, no one would treat a fracture without a follow-up X-ray for comparison as to alignment and status of healing. Comparative electrocardiograms are necessary requirements regarding medication for heart problems. Blood counts at the beginning and through treatment are expected for many medical problems. It goes on and on. But not in physical treatment. However, that was a small part of the problem at Irvine.

The clinical practice facilities for the faculty had not yet been fully organized. They were difficult to find, parking was complex, staff were indifferent—it was a mess. Moreover, the whole concept of having a university hospital fifteen miles from the main teaching hospital—the Orange County Medical Center, which was now the main campus of the medical school—was questionable. Indeed, the Dean who had hired me, who actually had been Chairman of Obstetrics, came under fire for those decisions and eventually was fired. The new Dean, an internist, felt the whole idea was crazy and, in spite of some significant contractual agreements, because of the power of the state government, was able to get a "divorce" from the Irvine Medical Center.

Looking for a New Job Again

I had been recruited to be Director of Orthopaedics at this new university hospital. Now my university appointment was of no benefit. The hospital hadn't opened yet and treatment programs were being carried out at the County Medical Center in the town of Orange, in Orange County. I wasn't able to generate sufficient clinical practice to reimburse my salary. My job was in jeopardy. Thus, I contacted an earlier mentor at Rancho Los Amigos—Dr. Lee Wiltse, who had a practice in Long Beach—as to the possibility that I might join him in practice part-time. That seemed to work out just fine from his standpoint. He was a well-known spine surgeon and had an excellent practice. There was a major flaw, however. Long Beach was about thirty miles from my academic offices at the medical school and forty-five miles from the Irvine Medical Center where I was to also have a practice. Only those of you who have experience with Southern California traffic can appreciate the complexity of the problem. Even then, in the late 1980s, congestion on the freeways was terrible. Travel times were totally unpredictable based on a single accident which might have occurred a half hour earlier and five miles ahead of you. Trying to be in three separate places in a single day, between Long Beach in Los Angeles County, mid Orange County at the medical school and the southern tip of Orange County at Irvine Medical Center, was a constant gamble. It gradually dawned on me that this was never going to work.

I started looking around for other opportunities. I had developed an unusual qualification which made me an attractive clinical faculty member. I understood the machinery of the California Workers' Compensation System. It turns out that care in the workers compensation system was the best reimbursed of all the health insurance systems utilized at that time—the early 1990s. How I got that knowledge was yet another unguarded moment.

When we moved back to California in 1988, my son, Mark, who had finished law school in Dallas at Southern

Methodist University, already had moved back and was in law practice in Los Angeles. It turns out that he was married to the daughter of the then California Chief Justice—Malcolm Lucas. More important than that, Lucas had been the law partner of the then Governor of California, Deukmajian.

Education in Workers' Compensation

About the time I had moved back to California, a new bureaucratic organization had emerged in an effort to control the spiraling costs of workers' compensation insurance. By law in all states, workers injured on the job had to have their medical expenses covered by the employer as well as being compensated during their period of disability. Naturally, the longer they were disabled and the more the medical expenses were to the employer, the cost of insurance had to go up. California had very generous regulations for the worker. This placed California in a very poor competitive situation compared to its neighboring states. If you could carry out a business in Nevada with the workers' compensation insurance half of what it would be in California, there had to be a considerable inducement for the businessman not to stay in California. During this period of time, many businesses were fleeing to Arizona, Nevada and New Mexico as well as Texas. All those states had better control on the workers' compensation expenses.

To try to reverse that trend, the California legislature had created a new commission to oversee workers' medical care. It was called the Industrial Medical Council. Typical of the cynicism of California politics, as originally set up, it was a fourteen-person commission. Seven of the physicians were appointed by the Republican governor and seven were appointed by the Democratic legislature. In general, the attorneys representing the injured workers, known as "applicant attorneys'', supported the Democratic legislators with considerable financial contributions. On the other hand, the business community supported the Republican governor. Thus, the people appointed by the governor were more conservative. Those appointed by the legislature often had ties to the applicant attorney community, who referred the majority of the patients. It was a setup for conflict. Especially with the 7/7 split, many times a vote could not decide an issue.

At any rate, coming to California from Texas and currently serving as a professor of orthopaedic surgery at a University of California Medical School, I brought no political baggage and, as a professor, some California credibility. When Governor Deukmajian became aware of my availability by the trail of connections mentioned above, I was appointed.

Naturally, I knew nothing about the system in California. The California system was different than any other state. Whereas most states used a system of identifying disability based on impairment, such as loss of joint motion, for musculoskeletal problems, California defined their disability awards based on pain. Impairment means loss of function, such as diminished range of motion, weakness, amputations, etc. It is objective. The system of defining impairment had been established and is known as the *American Medical Association Guides to the Evaluation of Permanent Impairment.* It is fairly detailed and an individual could have their impairment rated first as loss of upper extremity function and then, by a formula, converted into loss of whole person function. Each state had various formulae for converting the impairment number into level of disability.

Impairment actually does not equal disability in the musculoskeletal system. Impairment would equal disability

in the case of lost eyesight. The ophthalmologist would identify the percentage of loss by their formula, which would
pretty much describe the individual's functional loss. On the
other hand, take the loss of the fifth digit in a professional
piano player; thus, he is really disabled. That same loss in a
bricklayer is fairly minor. The more one looks into this dilemma, the more complex it gets. No state or, for that matter, nation has yet figured it out in a satisfactory way. Around
the world, there are many contrasting systems to reimburse disability.

In California, it was decided many years ago to forget
about the impairment and go directly to the usual cause of
loss of function in the musculoskeletal system—pain. To try
to make the system reproducible, rules were laid down as to
how the physician would define disability. For instance, pain
had to be defined at one of four levels: Minimal, slight, moderate and severe. Each implied an increase in affect on functional activity. Also, the physical had to describe the
duration of pain in terms of four levels: Occasional, intermit-
tent, frequent and constant. The report would not be acceptable unless those exact terms were used. Moreover, the
physician was expected to describe the percentage loss of
lift ability or work capacity after the injury compared to the
status before. Of course, the physician had not dealt with
the injured worker before the injury and really had only a
vague idea of what the capacity before the injury might be.
Nonetheless, he/she was expected to make an estimate. The
estimate was extremely important because that equated to
dollars of disability award. There were other factors which
went into the amount of disability award, which included
education, age and job, which did vary the amount of award.
Nonetheless, the majority definition of disability was based
on the subjective factors of pain. No one could really measure that.

One can easily see how that system can be misused. There are stories nearly daily in the press of some worker who was disabled with severe back pain and later was identified as a surfing champion somewhere. Or there are the cases of the person suffering a whiplash which has lasted for years and, after he/she gets the award, has an epiphany and suddenly gets better. The reality, from a scientific sense, is that pain is immeasurable. Actually, with improved MRI techniques, the centers of the brain which do generate the sensation of pain can be monitored and one's experience of pain can objectively be defined. That is only a recent development and certainly not practical in the world of disability management.

To try and adjudicate these issues of how disabled a worker might be, say from a back strain sustained six months earlier, a system of "independent" physicians was developed. They are called "Qualified Medical Evaluators". There are fairly strict criteria as to their qualifications and they have to take some training and pass an examination to be labeled as a Qualified Medical Evaluator. Of course, they are in all the specialties. In California, chiropractic doctors are recognized as legal physicians and therefore they also function as QMEs. There are two chiropractors on the Industrial Medical Council. There is a fee schedule, which is pretty good, and thus many doctors wish to carry on a practice as a QME. One of the early problems of the Industrial Medical Council was to try to develop systems to control the education and quality of the QMEs.

The monthly meetings of the fourteen members of the Industrial Medical Council were an education to me. I had not dealt with the issues of political and legal pressures before. The motivations of the various clinicians assigned to the Industrial Medical Council were always curious to me.

There were two psychologists, two chiropractors, another orthopaedic surgeon, and on it went. Each force seemed to balance the other. Little got done. More about that later.

The Start of Functional Measurement—Matheson

One bright spot during the time at UCI was the reconnection with Leonard Matheson, Ph.D. Years earlier, Len and I had interfaced some at Rancho Los Amigos Hospital. He was a psychologist working on issues of work capability. He had done some research with our patients on the Problem Back Service at Rancho. When we met again in 1989, he had a rehabilitation and test center in Orange County. He was developing some specific functional tests and needed a population of patients to compare the testing of normals. He developed a test known as the "Epic Lift Task". In an effort to objectively identify an individual's functional capacity, this was a test which evaluated how much they could lift. Progressive weights were placed in a milk crate and lifted in a standardized manner to shelves that were at knee height, belt height and shoulder height. After each cycle of lifting, the evaluee was asked if he could lift more. The weights that were used were bags of sand, all of the same size but weighing five, ten or twenty pounds. They were of different colors. Thus, the examiner knew how much weight was being lifted but the evaluee did not. Also, the heart rate was monitored to clarify the issue if the evaluee was making a valid effort. It is impossible to do progressively more strenuous activity without elevating the heart rate. If the evaluee said they could make no further attempts at lifting but had never elevated their heart rate, the implication was that no effort was being made.

175

At any rate, it was necessary to standardize the instructions to the people being evaluated. We set up a research project at the PAR Center in Irvine, where various ways of providing instructions were tested to identify those which gave the most consistent results. Standardization of the testing method is the key to gaining valid results. We also tested instruction to people being tested on the various strength machines. Again, consistency and reproducibility were important. These studies eventually got published and laid the groundwork for some significant work later. We'll see how that develops as the adventure unfolds.

But, the most significant unguarded moment of this entire story happened one night as I got home late. It had been a frustrating day. I had had my second martini—it was 7:30 P.M. A call came for me from a man in Florida—Arthur Jones. I vaguely knew who Arthur Jones was—he had invented Nautilus. I didn't know much more about him, other than that he had something to do with some medical exercise equipment. He was inviting me and Ruth to come out to his home in Ocala, Florida, and evaluate his new equipment, called "MedX"™. He would supply us both with first-class tickets for a weekend in Florida. I was just disgruntled enough to accept the offer—not knowing any of the implications.

Now, you will meet this remarkable character, Arthur Jones.

10

Arthur Jones, the Man Who Revolutionized the Health Club Industry

Before discussing our first meeting with Arthur, you need to know some details of his history. These are facts which I only learned later but are necessary background to explain what motivates the man. The first page of his autobiography is quoted below, a cryptic overview of some of his achievements. The title of the autobiography is *And God Laughs*. Arthur is by no means a religious man but a quote from Ecclesiastes, chapter 9, verse 11, serves as the prologue to the chapter and even his view of his life. "The race is not to the swift, nor the battle to the strong, nor yet bread to the wise, nor riches to men of understanding, nor yet favor to men of skill; but time and chance happeneth to them all." His life also was a series of unguarded moments. It was a search for opportunity. He did, however, change the way we exercise.

What follows are quotes from the opening chapter of his autobiography:

Having been a pilot for more than fifty years, it follows that the subject of flying will be involved in the following account but this is not a book about flying or pilots.

Having been involved in capturing, importing and selling exotic wild animals for periods of many years, it also

177

follows that such subjects will be mentioned, but this is not a book about animals.

Having founded and operated companies involved with a wide variety of activities, the subject of business will be mentioned, but this is not a book about business.

Having produced income of hundreds of millions of dollars, the subject of money is unavoidable; but this is not a book about money.

Having invented and sometimes marketed a wide variety of things in several fields, including Nautilus exercise machines, MedX™ medical testing machines, lenses, stabilizing camera mounts and editing machines for motion picture production and, along with some other things, the subjects of inventions and inventors also are included but this is not a book about my inventions.

Having filmed and produced and directed more than 300 films for television, as well as three theatrical films, the subject of film production will be touched on but this is not a book about the film industry.

Having at least visited almost every country in the world and having lived on four continents for long periods of time, the subject of travel will be involved but this is not a book about travel.

This book is not politically correct. It's a book about people, a few good people and along with some very bad people.

What follows in the autobiography is 351 pages of description of various adventures in business, marriage, discussion of exotic animals, especially rattlesnakes and alligators, and a lot about his sexual enthusiasm. The book depicts a truly driven man, who seldom sees his achievements appreciated, who frequently is cheated, who frequently is dealing with the rascals of the world and constantly fights to protect his ideas from being stolen.

Arthur—the Beginning

A psychologist would have a field day with his dysfunctional upbringing. His father was a doctor in Oklahoma and his mother went to medical school shortly after Arthur's birth. As he put it, "I had almost no contact with my father or mother from age three until fourteen, and no contact thereafter because, at age fourteen, I was gone from the home."

He had run away permanently. He states he was gone most of the time from eleven to fourteen. He defines his psychological dilemma quite well in that he states that these events were not really running away because his home provided him everything he needed and almost everything he wanted. He was driven to run toward something but he wasn't sure what. By the time he was fourteen, he had visited every state in the country, Mexico, Canada and British Honduras. He did this by hitchhiking, riding freight trains, tramp steamers and working here and there as he could.

As another demonstration of his independence, he and a friend built their own airplane at the age of fourteen—and it flew successfully. He started flying formally in 1939 and, by 1967, had logged 14,000 flights to every state in the country and fifty-six foreign countries.

By now, you get the picture of a man with a voracious curiosity. He read and still reads everything. He is fearlessly independent and truly a poster for the self-made man. As he states, politically, he is far to the right of Attila the Hun. He states that, when he was poor, government did nothing to help him but, when he was rich, it did everything possible to hurt him. He hated authority.

Before we get into the medical exercise story, a little more discussion of Arthur's other interests is appropriate.

During the Second World War, he was an air cargo contractor, flying transport planes around the world. That was necessary experience for his later work as a transporter of exotic animals and later wildlife photographer. He had developed a weird interest in reptiles and, from time to time, ran alligator and rattlesnake shows as a source of income. He was extremely knowledgeable about all forms of wildlife. On that basis, he developed great skills in capturing various animals, mostly in Africa, which were sold to zoos in America. Having gained skills in that area, he recognized his unusual area of knowledge, which could be transferred into production of shows about wild animals. He produced well over 300. Probably the most popular was *Wild Cargo,* which was a show on ABC television.

As an example of his unusual problem-solving skills and tenacity, he had to find a solution to the problem of how to get a wide-angle exposure of broad vistas of running packs of animals depicted from the air. At that time, there were no lenses which could capture the necessary vast width typical of the human eye. Cinerama had not been invented yet. Having studied the optical problem, he approached a lens maker in Germany with specifications of what was to be done. The lens maker insisted that it couldn't be done in that no lens like that was available. Nonetheless, with sufficient financial prodding, the lens was made and was a success. It is still used today. Another aspect of depicting wild animals from the air, be it by helicopter or fixed wing aircraft is the disturbing nature of flight. The aircraft always has some vibration. Clear pictures cannot be created. Here again, upon researching the project, he built a special tripod which dissipated the vibratory actions of the helicopter or plane so that a smooth view of the area being depicted was available. This is still used today.

He then saw himself in the business of movie production. He financed a production studio in Florida, which was state of the art, ahead of the time and technology compared to Hollywood and the television studios. This allowed him to control the production costs. For a period of time, this was a financially successful enterprise.

Most of the raw materials for his wild animals shows was in Africa, so he had a ranch in Zimbabwe, where he kept airplanes, some animals and an administrative office. At the time of the political upheaval in Rhodesia when the Europeans were thrown out of power by the African natives, his land was seized. He barely got out of Africa with his own skin and did not have all of his airplanes. He did fly out some elephants and other animals. He assumed that the seized resources would ultimately be returned to him but at that time he had little financial means of support. Actually, nothing was ever returned to him from the African seizure.

Arthur Stumbles into Exercise Equipment

As far back as 1939, he had been interested in trying to produce a more efficient mechanism of bodybuilding. Finally, he stumbled on a simple mechanical principle which extended the resistance throughout the entire arc of a muscle/joint movement. This was the cam wheel of increasing radius. He built his first piece of equipment in 1970. It was called the Blue Monster. At that time, he was unaware that exercise machines had been built by Gustav Zander in Sweden under the heading of medico-mechanical therapy. These flourished in the 1860s until the early 1900s. By the time Arthur became interested in this whole phenomenon, none of the Zander machines were being used anywhere around the world. He also was unaware that another exercise enthusiast named Hartz had even dreamed up the idea of a variable resistance with cam wheel in the 1880s and applied it to exercise equipment. This was not published widely and never became popularized. Timing is everything.

So it was in 1968 where Arthur had settled in Lake Helen, Florida, after he had left Rhodesia. He had assumed that the extensive photographic equipment that he had left there would be sent to him and he could start a new film studio. He was even in negotiation with Howard Hughes, who, at that time, was trying to buy one of the radio networks and decided to build his own network. At the moment, however, Arthur had nothing to do. He had recently sold a film titled *Operation Elephant* to the ABC network for $50,000. It would have cost the network at least a million dollars to produce it. It was a one-hour special and was aired in the fall of 1970 at very high ratings. Arthur decided to turn to writing. He wrote several stories about his own concepts of muscle function and bodybuilding. They were rejected by several magazines but *Iron Man* magazine, published by Peary Rader, accepted them. Rader was even quite excited about the concepts.

Arthur agreed to write several articles. He expected nothing but criticism from the readership. To his surprise, however, he got dozens of letters, which grew to thousands of letters, expressing interest in his ideas. A lot of his ideas dealt with the dose of exercise which could be achieved by specific exercise machines. None of these had yet been built and he never thought the machines would be commercially viable. He had conceived of them mostly for his own personal exercise. Nonetheless, with the interest expressed in the concept, he set himself to build such a machine.

The key innovative ingredient of the yet to be built exercise machine was the concept of a cam which could distribute an equal load over the entire range of a joint. The

182

concept really emerged when he was trying to explain a drawing of the gear box of the intended machine to his fifteen-year-old son, Gary. Gary looked at it and said it looked like a cam. Actually, that thought had not occurred to Arthur until that minute but he immediately realized that this was a possible solution to the problem of load distribution. Thus, Nautilus was born.

With six dollars and an overextended credit card as his total resource, Arthur, his children and, Inge, his assistant, drove to California for the annual Mr. America Contest and the National Weightlifting Championship. They drove straight through from Florida, alternating drivers. They were there to show off the Blue Monster. It was the prototype of the Nautilus machine. It was going to be held in Culver City, California, June 13–14, 1970. The machine arrived intact and it was a sensation. People wanted to order them. Timing is everything. The first Nautilus exercise machine was delivered in November 1970 with Arthur still owing $2500 to his sister, who funded the early construction. Fourteen years later, *Forbes* magazine listed him as among the 400 wealthiest people in America with an estimated net worth of $125 million. Although he had never planned to be in the exercise equipment business, obviously he had found a niche. Arthur far preferred the production of movies about wild animal adventures but this obviously was a growing business.

Arthur had made an exhaustive study of human physiology and biomechanics. He had observed that people with the longer muscles in a muscle-tendon complex, such as the calf muscles and the Achilles tendon, could build muscle faster. He came upon a young man at the Mr. America Contest, Casey Viator, with just that anatomy. He offered to train him. Casey won Mr. America the following year, in 1971. In fact, he won six of seven possible awards that year. After that, many emerging weightlifters and bodybuilders visited Arthur to be trained by his system. Among them was Arnold Schwarzenegger.

Early Confirmation of Arthur's Theories

An interesting spin-off of Arthur's concepts in training was his enthusiasm for eccentric training. He explained this in *Iron Man* magazine articles twenty years before it was in the physiology literature. That's what happens when the muscle is being used to slow the motion of a joint which is being pushed by gravity or additional weight. A good example of this is the shin muscles in the front of the lower leg, which are working harder than usual when you walk for long periods only downhill, such as going down a mountain. They always ache the following day. Nonetheless, muscle mass building is more efficient with eccentric exercise than the more common exercise, known as concentric used in any lifting activity.

Close to Lake Helen, Florida, where Nautilus manufacturing was established at that time, was Deland High School. Arthur got to know the coach and set up a protocol for eccentric training of the boys preparing for weight-lifting competition. Under this new regime, they took the state championship from 1973 to 1978. Their record from 1973–1992 was 622 wins, twenty-two losses and two ties. Two team members lifted the weight, which was then very gradually lowered by the teammate who was being trained. Rapid increases in strength and mass could be noted. Later they trained on eccentric loading with the Nautilus machine.

In another demonstration that brief but intense isolated exercise, especially eccentric, was all that was necessary to achieve remarkable changes in muscle physiology, in May of 1973, Arthur funded a research project supervised by the

Department of Physiology at Colorado State University in Fort Collins, Colorado, under the direction of Dr. Plese. Two people being evaluated were Casey Viator and Arthur. They trained at the gym in Fort Collins, equipped with Nautilus machines. They trained twelve times on Nautilus equipment, an average of three times weekly for four weeks. Casey gained sixty-three pounds of muscle, while losing nineteen pounds of body fat. Arthur gained forty pounds.

The following is an anecdote which depicts Arthur's pleasure in defining the fool. Arthur never learned to curb this capacity of brilliant people to challenge the sensibleness of lesser folks. At the Colorado experiment, a veterinarian had observed the great muscle gains and thought it was physiologically impossible. He demanded to know the secret. Arthur gave Dr. Plese a wink and said, "All right. You caught us." He went on to describe that, a couple of years ago on a trip up the Great Green Greasy Limpopo River in Africa, he came upon a group of black men never before noted by white men. They were huge. In an effort to find how this happened, he felt it must be the nutrition and therefore watched carefully what they ate. Actually, their nutrition was based on their religion. People on this island worshipped the great bull elephant and, in their nightly religious services, they consumed the feces of the elephants in order to demonstrate their subservience to the god. Obviously, this had to be the secret responsible for their unbelievable muscular development. The people on the other shore had a snake god but consuming snake shit did not have any effect on muscle mass. He tried to find the specific components but found it only worked with all the components working together.

The veterinarian said, "So, that's what you've been feeding Casey for the last four weeks?" Whereupon, he asked if we had any elephant shit left and offered to buy it from us for his own use. Arthur said, "Well, I think we have some left. It's as expensive as hell. We will sell it to you for what we paid for it."

He was ready to buy. Arthur could go no further and finally had to tell him the real story, that the muscle growth was based on exercise.

A week later, the veterinarian came by and talked to Dr. Plese and said, "You were just joking with me last week, weren't you?"

Plese said, "Of course we were joking."

The veterinarian said, "No, you misunderstand me. I mean, you were joking when you told me you were joking. The elephant dung really works, doesn't it?"

It's a wonderful story about how magic is easier to believe than physiology.

The West Point Study

The proof of Arthur's concepts about muscle training had to be confirmed to the scientific world. Even though the Colorado study was impressive, it was certainly not a scientific study. All of the information relating to the principles of strength training designed by Arthur Jones were published in the *Iron Man* magazine—not part of the scientific literature.

An unusual opportunity emerged. West Point Athletic Department, in early 1975, received a $50,000 grant to upgrade. Up to that time, the physical education room consisted of a few broken down barbells and coffee cans filled with concrete. A Sergeant Riley was in charge and he, himself, had grown up on barbell training and, typical of his era, his routine included two and a half hours a day of workouts. Captain James Peterson, a professor on the staff with a Ph.D.

in physiology, was assigned the job of upgrading the equipment. Peterson was not versed in strength training. He was aware of Nautilus, however, and contacted Arthur in Florida. He had planned to have a comparison between the other strength training equipment available at the time—Universal equipment—and Nautilus. The Universal equipment did not have the potential for eccentric loading, variable resistance, or muscle isolation. Universal, however, refused to participate.

West Point was an ideal location to carry out this type of research program. The subjects were all highly motivated, regimented young men. They chose to carry out the total conditioning project on even a more select group, the football team. The football coach, Homer Smith, was diametrically opposed to the use of exercise equipment and would not allow the first string players to participate.

Nonetheless, the study was developed with three groups. The whole body conditioning group had twenty-one cadets training three times a week. There was a neck training group with sixteen cadets, also training three times a week and, finally, there was a control group of sixteen cadets who were tested at the same intervals as the whole body group but had no coordinated training program except the one provided to them by the football team.

Cardiovascular fitness was also measured using submaximal work response measured on a bike ergometer and a maximal work response as well as capacity at rest, including heart rate, blood pressure and systolic tension time index. Body composition was measured. Strength was measured and various functional tests, such as a two-mile run, forty-yard dash and vertical jumping were measured.

The training, although intense, only lasted an average of thirty minutes a day. The cadets participated in the full regime of West Point, up at 5:00 A.M. and lights out at 11:00

P.M. They went through the rigors of academic training as well as the usual military skills. The study consisted of seventeen sessions over six weeks from April into May 1975. The last week of the study was also finals week.

The results were dramatic. The whole body group increased neck strength ninety-two percent compared to twenty-eight percent improvement in the control group and fifty-seven percent in the neck-only group. The two-mile run improved over four times as much as the control group. The forty-yard dash improved twice as much, the vertical jump height over four times as much.

The cardiovascular testing aspects of the study, including the testing, were set up by Dr. Kenneth Cooper and his staff. Dr. Cooper, of course, is the aerobics guru from Dallas. He stated that the program produced better results in six weeks than he had been able to obtain in ten years of focused effort. For years, he had been preaching that more is better and had openly criticized Arthur's strength training work. He recognized the value of Arthur's approach and subsequent publications confirmed it.

The important result of the study was that it confirmed Arthur's concepts concerning training. It had scientific credibility, being carried out in a totally independent environment. The West Point motivation was to identify the best training program possible. It had no connection at all with the equipment manufacturers and certainly not with Arthur. The director of the study, Captain James Peterson, had never met Arthur before the study, and was totally unaware of the controversies about him in the weight training literature. That probably is very fortunate in that this had become a very competitive industry and many lies were being circulated concerning Nautilus and Arthur personally. This was one of the few episodes in Arthur's history where his concepts did not fall under the IRACS principles. Arthur felt

188

that the fate of any new, valuable concept was for the rest of the world to Ignore, Ridicule, Attack, Copy, and, finally, Steal. Because of the credibility of the West Point study, this was not possible.

A broader benefit in the context of our story was that it confirmed that prolonged exercise training was not necessary. One could get excellent results with relatively short periods of exercise although it should be carried out with some intensity. In the role of therapeutic exercise, patient compliance is an important feature. If the amount of exercise required could be reduced and yet attain significant results, it would be more likely acceptable to the population.

Arthur had an unusual idea about selling. He recognized that he had ideas about muscle physiology and strength training which were not currently being used in the medical scientific world. It was his idea that the facts could be force fed to potential users/customers of strength training equipment, the Nautilus machines. He did this by flying doctors from all over North America to daily seminars. He did this at his own expense, using his own airplanes and pilots. He fed them for the day but they had to listen to the lectures about Nautilus. He did sell machines, but he offended many people by telling them what they didn't know. People don't like to be told they are stupid. It was intense work. Slowly, he was going through burnout.

The Birth of a Medical Testing Machine

He still didn't have a medical testing machine. According to him, by 1985, he had already built 3000 prototype machines and had invested forty million in research to try to come up with a better piece of equipment. Trying to convince medical professionals, he had a huge auditorium built on his farm north of Ocala, Florida, and had two multi-engine, jet-powered airplanes, which would pick up groups of medical professionals all over the country every morning, seven days a week, and fly to them to the airport he built on his own farm for a day-long seminar, taking them back in the evening. Thousands of medical professionals attended these seminars over a period of eight months from 1985 to 1986. 250 seminars were conducted. Orders were accepted for a forthcoming medical machine which hadn't been built yet. They, indeed, were too successful in that he had to halt them because he felt he would create more enemies than friends if the machines were not ready for delivery soon. He planned to start the seminars again but, as Arthur states, he made one of the biggest mistakes in his life—he sold Nautilus—largely because somebody made what seemed to be a reasonable offer when Arthur was basically used up—burned out.

A note about the airport is important here because it is one more demonstration of Arthur's imagination. It's the largest private airport in America. It could accept any size jet built up to that time, including a 747, yet it was not at FAA-prescribed length of over 7000 feet. Arthur solved this problem by elevating either end of the field by about fifty feet. Thus, when a plane landed, just as it was decelerating on the ground, the plane had to fight gravity as it climbed the hill. This slowed the plane down more rapidly. On the other hand, on the occasion of takeoff, racing downhill with the assist of gravity at the onset of takeoff gave an additional boost of power, which made the takeoff safe. Arthur says there is no other airport like that. What an idea! After all, he did get to the eighth grade.

Years later, Arthur sold the farm and the manufacturing plant adjacent to it. Now it's a private consortium with the landing strip surrounded by the homes of many celebrities from around the world, who take pleasure in a quick fly-in over the weekend, etc.

With Nautilus sold, he had a period of mental depression. With the assistance of a faithful supporter, Joe Cirulli, who owned a health club in Gainesville, they returned to work on a medical machine which could provide accurate measurement of spinal function. Arthur had long since given up on the credibility of isokinetic exercise, where the speed was measured, and isodynamic exercise, where position was measured but not controlled. He finally stumbled on measuring isometric strength at multiple points along the range of isolated cervical or lumbar motion. That became the MedX™ machine. It was a remarkable tool.

Here again, Arthur's instincts to go past the "authorities" and force feed the population got in the way of effective marketing.

In October 1987, at a well-established medical meeting, known as the "Challenge of the Lumbar Spine" in New York City, the first MedX™ lumbar machine was exhibited. To gain the doctors' attention, he published two page advertisements in *The Wall Street Journal, USA Today* and the *Washington Post,* entitled "A Partial Solution to an Annual 80 Billion Dollar Medical Problem." There were illustrations of test results produced by research at the University of Florida. The company did receive thousands of inquiries from these ads but these were from people with desperate back problems, not from doctors. To the experts in the field, it fell flat. As Arthur put it, this is the NIH approach, which is the typical response by almost any supposed expert in any field when presented by their peers with anything relatively new and not their idea. The NIH factor: Not invented here.

Although I didn't know it at the time, that's where I came in.

Searching for MEDX™ Credibility

Contrasted with the booming success of Nautilus, MedX™ sales were not going anywhere. The largest group of purchasers was chiropractors. Because a medical testing system was used in the treatment program, extra fees could be charged. Because it was a scientific piece of equipment which had the capacity to measure changes in function, the chiropractors saw this as an opportunity to enhance their scientific credibility. Most physical therapists had nothing to do with it. Some doctors who had had positive experiences with Nautilus did become involved but this was only a small number. Why Arthur turned to me, I'll never know.

Ruth and I were picked up at the airport in Orlando and driven out to Ocala. The young man driving us, Scott Leggett, was a graduate masters student at the University of Florida and had been involved with a large amount of MedX™ research already. This was directed by Michael Pollock, Ph.D., whom we will discuss later. On the way to Ocala, Scott asked a lot of questions about California, including the business of exercise physiology and therapy. I felt the scope of his questions was a little unusual. Years later, I found out that Scott, who had already received his masters degree several years earlier, felt that he was more or less spinning his wheels at the University of Florida, doing research on MedX™. He had mentioned to Arthur that he planned to look for opportunities elsewhere. Scott's funding at the University of Florida was by way of a grant from Arthur. Arthur told him not to make a move right away because he'd be working with Mooney in California. That conversation between Scott and Arthur had occurred about a year before Scott picked us up but, of course, he didn't mention it at the time. Scott, indeed, did move to California to UCSD when we set up the MedX™ treatment program with the

Department of Orthopaedic Surgery at UC San Diego. That was the result of this initial visit and a later visit by me with Arthur. It was 1990. Arthur also approached Byron Holmes, another student, months earlier to move to California.

Arthur had bought a huge section of land where he had put his auditorium and the air strip and the manufacturing facilities for MedX™. There already was what was called a farmhouse, which was really a mansion in the Southern style. Arthur had bought the holdings from someone with a shaky background, alleged to be a drug dealer. Little detail of his business has ever become available. One portion of his business, however, became apparent when Ruth and I were shown to our room in the big house. It was late and we were to meet with Arthur in the morning. I thought this was only in the movies but, honestly, the walls were red velvet. The ceiling above the bed had mirrors and the bathroom, which was huge, had a two-person bathtub in the middle of the floor. Ruth and I had not seen that before. Obviously, earlier owners were involved with diverse enterprises.

Arthur, who had several years earlier gotten a divorce from his fifth wife, was living in a small administrative building a short walk from the mansion. Since he didn't live there, when we explored the kitchen and refrigerator, there wasn't anything there. When breakfast came around the next day, it was really appreciated.

What Arthur wanted to show me was the remarkable ability of his equipment to isolate and clarify function for both the lumbar and cervical spine as well as torso rotation. We spent most of the time on the lumbar machine. This particular machine worked so that one did exercises in extension while sitting with the pelvis controlled so that it could not contribute to muscle forces. Internally in the machine, the torso weight could be counterbalanced so that any movement made by the individual was purely their own muscle activity, not assisted or deterred by gravity. The amount of isometric strength at points in range could be identified. By this time enough normals had been tested that the deviation from expected normal was known for each age group. Also, after repeated exercise, the amount of fatigue could be defined, which had some predictive characteristics. It was a whole mass of new information never before available to people evaluating neck and back problems. He showed me the research papers so far, some of which had already been published and some of which were awaiting publication. The ability of the lumbar muscles to respond to isolated extension exercises was remarkable. Correlation with improved patient function and reduced pain was just being demonstrated at the few centers already using MedX™ equipment. At that time, perhaps there were ten orthopaedic surgeons around the country who were using the MedX™ equipment.

Moreover, Arthur took me to the manufacturing facility, about half a mile away, and demonstrated how the things were put together. He knew the pitch of every screw and every dimension of every piece of metal. He knew how the computers worked. He had supervised and assisted in the design of everything. I was impressed. I agreed to come back later.

It had already been decided that I would be leaving UCI and joining the faculty at UCSD. Thus, I approached the Chairman of Orthopaedics at UCSD, Dr. Akeson, about the concept of bringing the exercise equipment and a training program to UC San Diego. That fit perfectly into his plans. The Orthopaedic Department had been relegated for years to a series of small Quonset huts with poor parking and dismal facilities. A new medical office building had just been completed, which was about half a mile from the proposed site of a new university hospital. With the potential for a donation of 1.5 million dollars worth of equipment, Dr. Akeson had some leverage in approaching the dean as to leasing space in the new office building. Both he and I knew that, if you can approach the dean with some "free" money, your leverage is far better than if you just say "I want . . ."

Because after this first visit I was convinced that this equipment was better than anything else I had seen, I wanted to be sure my judgement was correct. Thus, I later returned to Ocala, spent ten days with Arthur and then visited several facilities which already had the equipment. Ten days with Arthur was an education. He was the most brilliant man I had ever met. He had many varied ideas. He was constantly asking questions to see how much I knew. With frequent pleasure, he would say, "That's stupid." Nonetheless, I grew to have a great respect for this unbelievable mind. He never forgot a thing I said, and always remembered exactly the context in which it was spoken. He later sent me multiple books and letters to try to educate me. I seemed to be one of the few people who took pleasure in listening to him.

I asked him once who was his hero. Guess who? He was Nicolai Tesla. This was a Czech engineer who emigrated to the United States and showed up in New York City with two cents in his pocket to join Thomas Edison in his New Jersey laboratories. They worked well together at first but rapidly it became apparent that there was a significant disagreement in philosophy. Tesla understood that electricity could not be transmitted long distances by direct current because of the loss of energy due to the resistance in the wires. Surprisingly, the brilliant Edison did not wish to see that flaw with direct current and persisted with the concept that a new power plant every two miles would not be a problem. It was a classic example of NIH—not invented here. Eventually Tesla had to leave. He had demonstrated that electricity could be transmitted long distances using the phenomenon of alternating current. Two major enterprises were emerging—General Electric, with which Edison was associated, and Westinghouse Electric, with which Tesla became associated. Indeed, obviously the alternating current concept became successful. Also, Tesla designed many other phases of the use of electrical energy. For example, the dynamos at Niagara Falls were designed by Tesla. They were the largest in the world at that time. On it goes. His various ideas, however, were bought or stolen by others and this is why Arthur loved his story. Tesla died a pauper in New York City.

Another hero was Igor Sikorsky, the inventor of the helicopter. Sikorsky was a royalist in the First World War in Russia and designed four-engine bombers for the Russian air force. The pictures of these planes at the time looked like flying streetcars. Later on, he did design the Pan American airships which flew around the world. With various drawings, at that time he demonstrated that he had the basic idea of the helicopter during World War I but, just as Arthur, he did not have the opportunity or urgency to put it into practice then. Not until World War II did the idea of the helicopter come to fruition. It was a simple concept of a rotor blade that lifted and a smaller propeller perpendicular to the rotor, which could resist the torque created by the skimming rotor. In Sikorsky's original writings, he never saw it as a military tool but as a mechanism to salvage people who were trapped in places unavailable for any other mechanisms of relief. The delayed fruition of the idea demonstrated by the thirty-year hiatus between concept and achievement based upon the urgency of the time, to Arthur was a good example in the development of MedX™.

Now cometh my education on the subject of exercise physiology.

11

Do They Really Teach Restorative Exercise?—The Role of Exercise Physiology

Once I got used to the idea of MedX™ as an effective treatment for back pain, I started to look for some evidence behind the physiology of specific muscle strengthening. As described earlier, I was aware of the Cybex equipment and isokinetic test and training but there really wasn't much physiologic research supporting these methods of testing and training. Where was it for MedX™?

While visiting with Arthur, I was introduced to Michael Pollock, Ph.D. He ran the research lab at the University of Florida, Gainesville, which was carrying out studies on muscle function, especially in isolated and eccentric modes. Dr. Pollock had been recruited about 1985 to take over the exercise science department at the University of Florida. This was also associated with the medical school. The University of Florida, of course, was helped with the development of this department by a nine-million-dollar gift from Arthur to the university.

It was a brand-new program. Scott Leggett, who later joined me in San Diego, was their first graduate student. He had heard a lecture by Pollock and his younger associate, Jay Graves, Ph.D., shortly after his arrival at the University of Florida campus and volunteered to work with them. Scott stayed on after achieving his master's degree and became coordinator of clinical research until he left for California in 1991.

Michael Pollock had already had a long and distinguished career in the area of exercise physiology. Earlier, he had been director of the adult fitness laboratory at Wake Forest University in Winston-Salem, North Carolina. Even at that time, he was interested in exercise prescription for healthy adults as well as cardiac patients. The majority of interest in exercise physiology then was the measurement of cardiac function, which was transported into clinical usefulness by developing graduated and progressive exercises. Later, he became director of research at Kenneth Cooper's Institute for Aerobics Research in Dallas. He became president of the American College of Sports Medicine in 1982.

The Beginning of Medically Legitimate Therapeutic Exercise

Before discussing Mike Pollock's contribution to exercise training at the University of Florida, this is a good time to talk about the American College of Sports Medicine. As should be recognized by now, there has always been a blur as to the role of therapeutic exercise and fitness. This is especially related to the value of muscle strength as a part of the practice of medicine. Perhaps the individual most effective in sharpening the focus of the exercise role as related to medicine was R. Tait McKenzie.

He had received his medical degree from McGill University in Canada in 1892. He also had a degree in physical education from what then was known as Harvard's Hemenway Gymnasium. Under what was known as the Sargent System, exercise was measured with the use of anthropomorphic measurements which monitored physical weakness and deficiencies in performance. McKenzie was also a sculptor and produced two sculptures, one titled *The Sprinter* in 1902 and the other *The Athlete* in 1903, which heralded the ideal of physical attributes of a well-conditioned individual. He became chairman of the Department of Physical Education at the University of Pennsylvania in 1904 and made an important point in his opening remarks. He stated the gymnasium was for "the average man." Based on his earlier work, he had already evaluated 500 men to document baseline measurements of performance. He began to gather apparatuses which would allow exercise with gradually increasing difficulty, extending through the entire range of gymnastics. At that time, on the occasion of the opening of the gym, he enunciated a statement of policy which might still stand today as the basis of the American College of Sports Medicine. He stated that "The policy of the Department may thus be said to contain something of the hospital clinic, a great deal of the classroom and laboratory and a little of the arena." To demonstrate that, at the University of Pennsylvania, he taught students not only in physical education but in medicine and administered comprehensive physical examinations to individuals who would be engaging in physical education or sports activities.

Later, in writing an article in a classic text, titled *Athletic Training* (1914), by Michael C. Murphy, a famous track coach and trainer at University of Pennsylvania, McKenzie struck the important theme of exercise for everybody. He went on to say that the value to health of athletics and exercises is useful in training and preparation for the more gifted ones who wore the colors of their clubs, colleges and native land in athletic competition. There is, however, still value of a less strenuous form of exercise for those whose physiques were cast in a less heroic mold. (What a nice way to describe the rest of us!) Once the concept was accepted that exercise was appropriate for not just the athlete, the concept of therapeutic exercise of value to everybody was emerging. McKenzie wrote a classic text, titled *Exercise in Education and Medicine,* published in 1909, which tried to bring the focus onto those concepts.

These ideas were slowly bubbling through departments of physiology and physical education at various universities. One of the most important figures in this arena was Archibald V. Hill, who, in 1923, was appointed professor of physiology at University College in London. He put McKenzie's everyman concept into more precise terms. In his inaugural address upon taking of the chair, he stated that "setting up standards of physical normality in man was bound to prove to be a great advantage to medicine and to all activities of arts, where normal man is the object of study. The observation of sick men in hospitals is not the best training for the study of normal men at work. It is necessary to build up a sound body of trained, scientific opinion, first in the study of normal men, for such trained opinion is likely to prove the greatest service, not merely to benefit but in ordinary social, industrial life." Hill later would publish many significant articles on the physiology of muscle function, which are still important factors in our body of knowledge. Still, most of the testing was done with treadmills and bicycle ergometers, studying the energy transformation and the oxygen exchange, etc. Actually, there was no way to measure isolated muscle function unless one would turn to machines such as Zander's equipment. Apparently these were unknown in the research laboratories of the time.

This type of research, however, did develop some important generalized principles. Tait McKenzie had published an article in 1906, titled "The Relationship of Athletics to Longevity", which documented that the strenuous efforts of prolonged athletic endeavor had a positive effect on longevity. He provided evidence that the athletic heart was really a healthy heart.

As usual in such situations, the importance of these concepts of fitness did not hit home until the need for fit young men was clearly identified, i.e. world wars. Twenty percent of the men recruited for World War I were considered physically unfit for duty. Similar figures were published for World War II. This, as would be expected, allowed government programs to emerge with focus on fitness. As an outgrowth of that and numerous government commissions, during the Second World War, public schoolteachers and college instructors devoted class time to chinups, pushups, dips, rope climbs and running events. Mass calisthenics were also incorporated into daily gym classes because of conditioning value and usefulness in developing quick response to commands. Awareness certainly was emerging. But, due to cost cutting, these exercise events have generally faded from the public school system.

The Beginning of Sports Medicine

The world of sports medicine was likewise growing. Of course, early in the development of college athletics and much later in professional athletics, physicians were assigned as team surgeons. Their assistants, at that time known as "rubbers", were the early athletic trainers. Their name identifies their expected role of massage therapists. At this early time, a professional association of a physician with athletes was thought to be a little undignified for a doctor of medicine. How the pendulum swings! Now medical groups pay millions to be identified as the "team physician" for various professional teams.

Because of that early opinion, books and journals focused on treatment of sports-related injuries did not appear until the 1930s. It wasn't until 1953 that the American Medical Association developed a committee on injuries and sports. Still, the interest was growing. Surprisingly, the famous Yale football coach, Walter Camp, wrote an article titled "Training for Sports" in 1921 (he initiated the Heisman Trophy). The first time trainers started to get organized relative to sports injuries was the formation of the National Athletic Trainers Association in 1938.

It was not until 1954, however, that the various groups interested in physical fitness, health and sports medicine came together. Initially, the group was titled "The American Federation of Sports Medicine" but changed the name to "The American College of Sports Medicine" in 1955. It was a coalition between therapists, scientists and physicians. Seven of the founding members were exercise physiologists and three were cardiologists. The influence of the cardiologists continues to be strong and the first several presidents were internists. The first physiologist to the president of the American College of Sports Medicine did not occur until 1960. This was Dr. Bruce Dill, who had been a pioneer researcher in exercise physiology at the Harvard Fatigue Laboratory. Reflecting an even broader confederation in the membership, Henry Montoye of the physical education department at Springfield College became president in 1962. Nonetheless, as time passed, the major interest was concerned with sports performance, injury prevention and injury treatment. It remains today a very healthy, eclectic conglomeration of various professions interested in fitness.

This brings us back to Michael Pollock. In that he was funded essentially by Arthur Jones by way of the University of Florida grant, and he had a unique piece of equipment, a Nautilus leg extensor tensometer, the original research was focused on understanding isolated muscle training. The original research clarified the issues of isometric strengthening at various points of range as being only effective in these various points. This was a totally new arena of research in that, as mentioned earlier, specific equipment for isolation of muscle function had not been available. Later on, when the MedX™ spinal equipment became available, extensive testing for lumbar and cervical strength was carried out, published in numerous venues.

Based on this research, Pollock was convinced of the value of resistance training and, because of his eminence in the field of sports medicine, he was able to get published the first guidelines for resistance training of various muscles. He had earlier been instrumental in developing guidelines for aerobic and cardiac training and is still known in the physiology world for the Jackson-Pollock method of evaluating percentage of body fat using calipers.

The majority of the membership of the American College of Sports Medicine did not have access to specialized exercise equipment and took little interest in the area of specific resistance training. It remains the case today that, although the guidelines persist in the publications of the ACSM, they are more or less sidelined. The main interest still concerns fitness rehabilitation of the cardiac system and general exercise programs.

Dr. Ted Dreisinger and Resistance Exercise

This was all news to me, however. I was unaware of schools of exercise science until interfacing with Dr. Pollock, Scott Leggett and other graduates of the Florida school. As was mentioned earlier, I was encouraged to visit other facilities which had MedX™ equipment. I was very happy to do so because I wanted to be sure that my agreement to initiate an exercise program at the University of California San Diego under the auspices of the Orthopaedic Department was justified. One of the first places I visited was in Columbia, Missouri. There, I met Ted Dreisinger, Ph.D.

Ted was Canadian. He trained in the United States as an exercise physiologist. He had a Ph.D. and was expert in cardiac training protocols. He had been recruited by an orthopaedic group in Columbia, Missouri, to establish a spinal rehabilitation program. This was 1987. At this time, spinal surgery in the form of fusions for back pain was blossoming. The concept of a Spinal Center was developing. It became apparent that patients were quite disabled both before and after the surgery and certainly there was justification to try to find some mechanism to achieve rehabilitation. Actually, the story of how Ted got to know Arthur and eventually chose MedX™ equipment for the Spine Center in Columbia, Missouri, is another example of serendipity—a series of unguarded moments.

After serving his time in the Vietnam War as an air traffic controller, Ted returned to West Virginia, where he had been in college prior to being sucked up into the War. He went to Fairmont State College, where he found that the quickest way to get a degree was in physical education as a major with an English minor. Thus, having no plan before to be involved with anything related to exercise, because he did have the GI Bill, he had an opportunity to get a college degree.

Following that, he got his master's in exercise science at the University of Wisconsin at La Crosse. There were still few such schools around the country but La Crosse was one of the best. Another was in Springfield, Massachusetts. Another, of all places, was at Slippery Rock State Teacher's College in Pennsylvania. The difference between degrees in physical education and exercise science was that phys. ed. graduates expected to be teaching in high schools, etc., whereas exercise science graduates expected to be involved with health clubs and cardiac rehab. Dreisinger later went on to get his Ph.D. in exercise physiology.

Ted and a colleague started a company called Value Life Associates, which produced a series of wellness training seminars. The idea of wellness had not quite emerged in the 1980s and they were a bit ahead of the curve and were unsuccessful.

Now, here's the next unguarded moment. Because of his company, Ted had left his business card with the head physical therapist at a hospital in Columbia, Missouri. The major spine surgeon—Dr. Garth Russell—the next day in the elevator, talking to the physical therapist, asked her if she was aware of anybody who could write scientific literature. She had just received the business card the day before and handed it to Dr. Russell. Dr. Russell contacted Ted the next day and he was recruited to write scientific papers for Dr. Russell. Garth was trying to climb into political eminence as an internationally recognized spine surgeon and had to therefore submit papers and make presentations at national and international meetings. He had no time to collect the data and write the paper and write the bibliography, etc. Ted had been trained to do this and, even though he had absolutely no knowledge about spinal care, the principles of scientific paper writing were quite familiar to him. He thus was successful in that role, especially as a ghostwriter. This was in 1987.

Actually, Garth Russell had little interest in rehabilitation of any sort but his colleague and protégé, Dr. Tom Highland, was passionately interested. In order to maintain this valued colleague at the Columbia Spine Center, he wanted to pursue the goal of having a Spine Center including rehab capacity. Garth and Ted visited several facilities which had the equipment available at that time. The equipment was made by various companies such as Lido, Iso Dynamics and Cybex. Coming from his cardiac rehabilitation background, when visiting these centers Ted was always confused by the lack of protocols in the use of equipment. This was a consistent observation as he questioned the therapists at these various centers. Moreover, measurement of lumbar function was done in a poorly controlled, dynamic manner, which had potential for injury.

When one measures functional strength, obviously it is necessary to encourage the patient to do their best effort. If this is done too violently in somebody who already has a back problem, injury seemed likely and thus Ted was not sure that the equipment was of value. Although Garth wanted to proceed and purchase the equipment (money was really not a restraint in this case), Ted was insecure and encouraged Russell to wait a little longer. (Four or five years later, these pieces of equipment were more or less condemned by a classic scientific article by Newton and Waddell, which pointed out the same flaws that Ted had observed.)

Thus, Ted was encouraged to go to Florida and visit other locations where it was known that spinal exercise equipment was being used. The Shands Hospital in Gainesville, Florida, was just such a location.

When Ted and Jan Weber, the physical therapist at the Columbia Hospital, were in Florida, they visited with Mike Pollock at the University of Florida in Gainesville. Dr. Pollock's work was well-known to Ted Dreisinger in that he had written widely concerning cardiac rehab protocols. When Pollock learned of the main purpose of the Dreisinger visit—a search for appropriate spinal exercise equipment for a new spine center, he told them to go visit Arthur Jones.

As you remember, Arthur was funding Pollock's work on strength evaluation by a large grant to the University of Florida.

An appointment was made to visit Arthur. Ted and Jan Weber met with him. It was a fairly brief visit. Arthur was unusually caustic and degrading to both of them. He was especially nasty to Jan Weber, portraying her in insulting terms and saying such things as that, although he recognized that orthopedic surgeons were dumb, he thought physical therapists were far dumber. Little progress was made there. However, Arthur said, "Why don't you come by and have lunch when you go by here on the way to the airport?" A couple of days later, after they finished their evaluation of the centers in Florida, they were on the way to the airport to go home to Missouri. While driving past Ocala, where Arthur had his facility, Ted turned to Jan and queried her if they should go ahead and have lunch as they had been invited. She certainly had been insulted several times and Ted had felt uncomfortable but, with the attitude of "why not", they pulled into the driveway at Arthur's place. There he was, sitting in the car, waiting for them to show up, knowing all the time that they would return for lunch. While at lunch on that day, Ted asked Arthur why he had been so obnoxious on the occasion of their first visit. Arthur paused a while and then said, "Ninety percent of the people who visit want something from me. Ten percent want to learn something from me. This is my way to avoid wasting time." All things considered, I guess that's not such a bad strategy.

Ted went home. He still did not have a clear idea how he would put together a spinal center and really didn't yet know how to digest Arthur. One night, he was driven to call and he did—it was after midnight in Florida. Arthur answered the phone and said, "Why did you call?"

Ted said, "I don't know." There were two minutes of silence and then Arthur proceeded to have a two-hour discussion as to the physiology of exercise and the value of the MedX™ system designed by him. Ted then encouraged Garth Russell to buy the equipment and that became the Columbia Spine Center. This started a whole new education for Dreisinger. As described, his entire prior education experience had been in cardiac rehab, general exercise and wellness but none of it had been in strength training. He certainly was familiar with protocols because he had helped set up several cardiac rehab centers in hospitals throughout Missouri. Reimbursement was based on the use of protocols and the demonstration of improved function from a cardiovascular standpoint, and thus the protocols were designed to document improved function so that there would be no question of insurance reimbursement. (Isn't it amazing how that simple phenomenon of requiring improved function before awarding additional care has never been a feature for reimbursement of the physical therapy in the musculoskeletal system?)

There could not have been two more contradictory personalities. You already have heard about Arthur. He was the most profane man I had met. On the other hand, Ted was very thoughtful. He is quite spiritual. He and his wife were heavily involved with a church in Missouri. He was the son of a Baptist minister. He never said an obscene word. He never said a harsh word about anybody. Yet, they grew to respect and trust each other. As a mark of respect for Ted, from then on whenever they had conversations together, Arthur never used a cuss word or obscene word again. Arthur continued to use extremely foul language in public, often using the "f" word several times in a sentence. Perhaps this was some sort of defense mechanism. He seemed to enjoy offending everybody. Never did he wish to offend Ted again.

Ted, of course, with his background of exercise physiology expertise, was instrumental in developing standardized protocols for training. He went on to develop his own MedX™ Center and later to set up spine training centers in hospitals much as he had done in setting up cardiac rehab facilities twenty-five years earlier.

The Value of Training Protocols and Dr. Pollock

At the Columbia Spine Center, I was worked out on the equipment, saw the entire layout of their rehabilitation facility and, of course, got ideas of how we should develop ours in San Diego. Right away, Ted and I developed a friendship. He was constantly enthusiastic. Because of his extensive background in exercise physiology, he had a large area of knowledge which was unknown to me. We could have long discussions as to the physiology of what was really going on on the occasion of isolated exercise of the lumbar and cervical musculature. It was a totally new learning experience. I now had developed a significant respect for the whole field of exercise physiology, but recognized that only a few of these trained personnel had a background in resistance training.

At each place I visited, muscle testing was done on me after an exercise program on the MedX™ equipment. Arthur insisted on this, recognizing that a documentation of significant change would be notable. Actually, this is quite unique for the area of therapeutic resistance exercise. As we know, an EKG done in Sacramento could be read by a doctor in New York City. The principles were constant. Up to that time, there were no set principles for reading the function of a specified muscle group and the progress of training. Because there were standardized protocols in the use of

MedX™ equipment, this was quite available. Thus, in each place I visited, I brought along the printout of my performance, which had recorded the previous performances and the new performance at the new facility was placed in position by the computer. Totally unique. It was not available in any other system. That's the case today. Somebody who shows up at our facility who has been MedX™ trained in New Haven, Connecticut, for instance, and brings their printout of performance can be placed upon the treatment program without a missed step. The left hand knows what the right hand is doing.

The next place I showed up was in Orange County. Another exercise physiologist, Ed Collins, had taken over a rehabilitation facility know as SCAR (Southern California Athletic Rehabilitation). It had been started some years earlier by several orthopedic surgeons as a sports medicine and rehabilitation facility using Nautilus equipment. They had found other areas of interest and Ed had taken it over, purchasing MedX™ equipment. Once again, I worked out on the equipment and again demonstrated my increasing strength in the lumbar spine based on specific exercises. SCAR still is an excellent training facility in Orange County and we often refer patients there.

In all, I had visited four different facilities, two in Florida, one in Columbia, Missouri, and one in Orange County. Each gave a very similar picture of effective care for chronic back and neck problems based on MedX™ training. I was greatly reassured that the judgement to use the equipment at the Orthopaedic Department at University of California San Diego was appropriate. We received shipment in early 1991.

And this brings us back to Dr. Michael Pollock. He was the first one to supply documentation as to the efficacy of the specific training programs utilizing isolated eccentric and concentric exercises to the lumbar extensor muscles and the cervical muscles. He was a researcher with a long-term view of the role of research. Once established, he never changed the protocol of testing. If one would do so, this would ruin the value of data comparing early results with later results. His goal was to have data ten years after the initial experience. He was the ideal researcher to be involved with the basic research and later the training programs for MedX™. Initially, the work was carried out on normals and documented unusual increases in strength in the lumbar extensors, unknown with strength training of any other muscles. The low lumbar extensor muscles do function a little differently than the other muscles. It was on the basis of this information that Arthur thought he had discovered the key to the resolution of back pain. He was sure that he should receive the Nobel Prize for this! (Actually, given the social and economic aspects of chronic back pain—that wasn't such a far-out idea, but impossible given the disrespect the scientific community had for Arthur Jones.) There was, indeed, a significant respect for Michael Pollock and he continued to produce a series of papers with the graduate students.

Unfortunately, he had developed rheumatoid spondylitis and had less and less mobility and could carry out less and less vigorous physical activity himself. Nonetheless, he was effective in directing research and, due to his diligence in maintaining the same protocols and always searching for comparative data to demonstrate the relevance of the new data, a multitude of publications emerged. While attending a scientific meeting in 2000, he had an apparent heart attack—perhaps based on medication—and did not survive. What a loss for the credibility of this whole project.

Some of the research still remains unpublished. He demonstrated very clearly that specific strength training on the spinal structures using isolated eccentric and concentric exercise could reverse osteoporosis and increase bone density. It had been demonstrated that resistance exercises were a better form of exercise to maintain stimulation of bone formation than passive exercises. He had supervised a study on patients who had received heart transplants and had therefore taken medication to resist immunological abnormalities which would cause rejection. It was well-known that these medications, however, would drop the bone density twenty-five percent. In the study, half of the people over six months received progressive resistance training and returned their density to near normal, even while on their medication. Those who received no exercise but also continued on the medication continued to have loss of bone density. He had several other studies that did not get to be published on more normal people with known causes for osteoporosis who were placed on exercise programs and did increase their bone density.

The basic strength of Michael Pollock from the very beginning was the recognition of the value of testing and training the ordinary person and not just the athlete. The ordinary person was the individual who would get degenerative lumbar and cervical disc disease. What was their baseline performance was a key question in identifying a rational treatment program for the future. He emphasized that to his graduate students and the basis of the data produced could get it published, usually in well-regarded scientific journals. He therefore established the protocols which are currently used today in MedX™ training for chronic neck and back pain, using equipment which generally requires only two sessions a week and generally will resolve the problem within eight weeks. Without Michael Pollock's attention to detail to document clear cut benefits of one protocol versus another, this information would never be visible. No other form of musculoskeletal exercise has as much documentation as to the benefits of a specific protocol versus another. These are contained in Dr. Pollock's series of publications relative to MedX™ training for the cervical spine and lumbar spine.

To Arthur's credit, he never interfered with the research or published results by Dr. Pollock. They did not always conform to Arthur's zealous expectations. He was responsible for research funding. He never modified a word in the publications.

12

Now to UC San Diego—Show Them
It Works

After the grand tour of four MedX™ facilities and two pro-longed visits with Arthur in Ocala, Florida, I was personally convinced that this equipment was a significant step forward to spine care and justified to be in a university physical therapy setting. Although the qualities of the equipment were essentially unknown to the rest of the Orthopaedic Department and, for that matter, the university bureaucracy, they needed little convincing. Arthur's offer to donate $1.5 million worth of equipment to the university was really all that had to be said. In a perfunctory show of due diligence, it was decided that an assistant dean, an assistant hospital administrator and the chairman of the Department of Orthopaedic Surgery should make a visit to Florida to confirm the deal. I was invited to come along as well.

Arthur was, surprisingly, on his best behavior. He showed them around the ranch and the manufacturing facilities and gave a brief description of the equipment. He took us all out to dinner and was really quite the host. He didn't use the "f" word more than two or three times. The administrative types were duly impressed and left the following day with a simple contract that Arthur provided them, saying that he had donated certain pieces, worth $1.5 million retail, to the University of California at San Diego—Orthopaedic

Department. The equipment was thus donated to the university and not to me personally, which becomes an interesting problem later on. All went home happy, except for Arthur. I know how he hated bureaucracies and he was grinding his teeth all the time of the visitation. Worse than that, one of the administrators had acquired six towels from the bathhouse next to the swimming pool. It's not that he cared about the towels necessarily, it just confirmed his views of the responsibility of a bureaucracy.

The equipment arrived along with Scott Leggett and Brian Holmes. Brian was a recent graduate from the University of Florida Exercise Science program and was pleased to be sent to California for a change of pace. If we were to set up a treatment program using MedX™ equipment, it was necessary that there at least be two knowledgeable therapists involved, so that someone was always involved in the treatment program. And that became a problem—the treatment program.

The Orthomed Center Evolves

The space in La Jolla also was to serve as a training center for the use of MedX™ equipment. Arthur, in addition to the donation of equipment to the University, also subsidized this with the salary of a trainer/educator. She also served as a clinical researcher. It was anticipated that the OrthoMed Center associated with the Orthopaedic Department at UCSD would be a training center for the MedX™ equipment on the West Coast. The University of Florida has the one on the East Coast. Thus, as time passed, we put on several classes for therapists and physicians who were purchasing MedX™ equipment.

These educational opportunities were provided with purchase of equipment. No other company did that. These classes not only included the technical aspects of the use of the equipment, which was not too complicated, but also specific discussion of our clinical experience and the ways it could be applied for various medical problems. This also supplied a mechanism wherein all the new therapists joining us would be brought up to speed with the protocols and techniques of this equipment. In addition, it supplied some of the resources to carry out clinical research projects. Arthur Jones never got any credit for this but he was glad to endorse it in that he certainly wished to scientifically prove the validity of his concepts as expressed in the MedX™ equipment. He already was supporting considerable research at the University of Florida with Dr. Pollock. As noted earlier, in neither case did he ever make any attempt to modify the results or correct any manuscript. I doubt that you can say that about the drug studies which are supported by the huge pharmaceutical companies.

There already was a Physical Therapy Department attached to the University Hospital. They were not pleased with the invasion of the Orthopaedic Department. They had their own physical therapy program—not using exercise equipment. They resisted from every angle. They tried to mobilize the state physical therapy association to declare us illegal. However, with physician supervision, exercise science people could carry out treatment programs which would be reimbursed by the usual payors.

They fought us for space, declaring the space not being used in a building assigned to the physical therapists as unavailable. We had to make alternative arrangements. Nonetheless, we did have the trump card in that, with all the equipment arriving from Florida—now owned by the Orthopaedic Department, we had resources. We had to have the opportunity to use it. It had to be placed somewhere. The building into which the Orthopaedic Department was moving was just being finished and, though there were several months of lag time, finally the equipment was placed in a brand new facility, not far from the new University Hospital, which was being built in La Jolla.

In that the space leased by the Orthopaedic Department was much larger than was necessary to carry out the clinical practice alone, most of it was used for therapy and the education programs. It was necessary to name the area for appropriate signage. I suggested to Dr. Akeson, the Department Chairman, that we call it the OrthoMed Center. Literally translated, that meant straight medicine. Also it resonated with the orthopaedic logo, which depicts a growing tree (symbolizing a spine) being straightened by ropes around a straight stake in the ground. I hoped it would also imply honest care.

Multiple pieces of equipment were placed around the large room, which was now the therapy section of the Orthopaedic Department. We had more equipment than was actually necessary but some was intended to be used as training equipment for the expected courses in the use of the MedX™ equipment. The center really looked very good. The Orthopaedic Department had a proud open house.

The battle with physical therapy wasn't over. They were located in the University Hospital, and in that much of the Orthopaedic Therapy is outpatient, their impact was gradually diminishing. They resisted any transfer to the Orthopaedic Center.

To everyone's astonishment, the OrthoMed Center became quite successful financially in that, because we used exercise equipment and standardized protocols, fewer and less expensive therapists were necessary to carry out the treatment program. We did, indeed, hire an appropriately trained physical therapist who also had a degree in exercise science. However, our personnel cost per patient was less than standard physical therapy centers. Gradually, we grew to have an annual net profit of about $250,000. This was translated into various research programs which were published—documenting the benefit of progressive resistance exercise as a treatment for spinal disorders as well as for extremity problems.

Documentation of Efficacy

At this time, now the mid-90s, it was clear that postoperative care for a shoulder or a knee that had been treated arthroscopically would require progressive resistance exercises. It was not very clear that progressive resistance exercises provided before surgical care might avoid the need for arthroscopic surgery for such things as shoulder impingement syndrome, arthritic knees and ligament deficient knees in older patients. With the equipment, we could make some inroads into the orthopaedic traditions of care.

There are several problems in musculoskeletal care which are somewhat unique. Since most of the limitation in the non-athletic population is pain which limits function, it is often difficult to separate the benefits of treatment as perceived in the short term by the patient versus true improvement in function. This brings in the whole question of the charisma of the treater. This is even a problem evaluating postoperative results. If the patient has built a bond with their therapist or surgeon, they are often embarrassed to say that the treatment hasn't worked out as well as expected and that there is disappointment with the results. Certainly, some personalities are more amenable to the healing arts than others. Some therapists and doctors are more likable than others. Such realities are confounding factors if one is trying to identify the best treatment.

To try to answer that particular question—the difference between charismatic care and effective care, we launched an extensive clinical research project with colleagues in Minneapolis. Dr. Brian Nelson had several facilities in Minneapolis, named "Physician's Back and Neck Clinics". His use of MedX™ equipment predated us by about a year. We both were using essentially the same protocols in terms of spinal measurement and advancing of resistance exercises as had been identified by the research work out of the University of Florida, guided by Dr. Michael Pollock. On the other hand, our programs were formatted somewhat differently. All the patients in the Minneapolis program had been evaluated by a limited number of physicians employed at the clinics and referred to physical therapists who carried out the treatment. At the San Diego facility—the OrthoMed Center—patients were referred from multiple physicians and, although initially evaluated by physical therapists, the treatment was carried out largely by exercise physiologists. Thus, the only phase of treatment which was consistent for the spinal problems was the protocol using MedX™ exercise equipment.

The study was finally published in the *Spine* journal in 1997. Initially, it included 1100 patients at UCSD and about 900 patients in Minneapolis. All had failed previous physical therapy and chiropractic and twelve percent had previous surgery. In order to have a comparable study, all had to have the same amount of treatment, which was two exercise sessions per week for twelve weeks. About a fifth of the initial group left early. About twenty percent of that group that left early found that the treatment wasn't helping. On the other hand, about forty-five percent of that leave-early group found they were doing so well they didn't need the twelve weeks of treatment.

Other issues emerged, which are always factors in trying to run a clinical research study. About ten percent felt there was no time or had transportation problems. Six percent found that it was too expensive. Eight percent didn't like the program and four percent had such severe pathology that they needed to go on to have surgery. On the other hand, the results of both centers were very similar in terms of efficacy. At UCSD, ninety-five percent felt they were satisfied with medical care and, in Minnesota, ninety-six percent were, three percent were made worse after they completed the program at UCSD and four percent in Minnesota. On the other hand, seventy-two percent were made better (having failed previous physical treatment) in Minneapolis, while eighty percent were better at UCSD. Both had about the same percentage change in pain in intensity at discharge and both groups were better one year after discharge.

The reutilization of the healthcare system for a back problem at one year follow-up was twelve percent at UCSD and thirteen percent at Minneapolis. Those who were made worse could not improve their strength, while those who were made better had significant improvement in strength. The study clearly documented that the personality of the treaters was of minimal significance, and the progress of treatment by strength increase protocol was reliable.

In addition to measurement of function, it is necessary to measure general health status. There is a standardized test which is well-accepted in the medical literature, known as the "SF-36" (short form with 36 questions), which had been used to evaluate the health status of many medical problems, ranging from arthritis to diabetes to musculoskeletal conditions. It measured eight different aspects, including perception of pain, psychosocial interaction and general sense of wellness. The results here also were consistent. The UCSD scores were just about the same as those in Minneapolis. Those who improved function on the MedX™ equipment also showed significant improvement in the scores on the SF-36. Those few that did not improve showed little change in the SF-36 scores. We felt that this totally justified the type of treatment being offered.

The specific protocols to advance strengthening must have made a significant difference since, despite the fact that all the patients included had failed previous nonoperative and operative care, the high level of successful results was about the same at two totally different centers using varying formats. Thus, documentation of efficacy was clearly demonstrated. Personality helps, but appropriate training is better.

We explored other projects to demonstrate efficacy. In an article published in the *Journal of Spinal Disorders* in 1997, where we did EMG studies of the extensor muscles, tested their strength and evaluated the muscle mass by MRI, we compared the patients to an equal number of normals. We discovered by the MRI studies that people with chronic back pain have a lot of atrophy in the small extensor muscles of the lower lumbar area, known as multifidus. The muscles are infiltrated with excessive fat. The muscles around them, however, do not have the same atrophy. Also, we demonstrated that the amount of electrical energy applied to the muscles through the nervous system decreased by fifty percent for the same resistance at the conclusion of the exercise training program. The muscles function more efficiently. The training program for both normals and chronic back patients was two sessions a week for eight weeks. Extensor strength improved forty-eight percent in the chronic pain patients, while it improved about six percent in the normal patients. All the chronic back pain patients improved their function and reduced their pain.

Several other studies were carried out, demonstrating that, although you couldn't predict onset of back pain in a population of workers—in this case shipyard workers—by strength testing, once they had back pain, their lumbar extensor strength was reduced. We also demonstrated that wearing a weight-lifter's belt while doing strength testing made no difference. For a strip mine in Idaho, a study was done which demonstrated that workers who did strength training once a week did not have any back injuries, while those who did not choose to carry out the strength training had a significant number of back injuries. Multiple other studies were carried out, demonstrating the efficacy of strength training, especially with the specialized equipment that Arthur Jones had designed. The confidence that I gained in observing the various treatment programs around the country was reinforced by our experience.

We Try the Health Club Approach

On the other hand, this "new" mechanism of treatment had not yet been appreciated by the medical community in general and specifically many of the insurance carriers. The new concept was that physical training takes time. Even well-trained athletes come to training camps at least six weeks before they start playing the serious games in order that additional physical training can get them in shape. Compare that to the problem of the ordinary population, who in general is not nearly so fit as these athletes. How long will it take them to get in appropriate shape?

Unfortunately, many of the contracts signed by the University for reasonable economic reasons did not choose to recognize this reality. For instance, many of the HMOs contracting with the University physicians would allow only three to four visits for chronic recurrent back pain or other chronic musculoskeletal problems. Of course, that's not enough to carry out an appropriate physical training program. On the other hand, patients funded by workers' compensation often would be allowed two to three years of ineffective passive physical therapy with hot packs, ultrasound and manipulation. The cynical views of the doctors knew that it was "fake and bake" therapy but it kept the patient complaints down and coming back for continued consultations. How could we resolve this problem? I will discuss the workers' compensation later but, for the managed-care patients in the University practice, another strategy emerged.

Many of these patients were members of the University community as faculty members, technicians, administrative assistants, etc. Once displayed and demonstrated, they could understand the concepts of a gradual progressive physical training program using exercise equipment. They recognized that an adequate training program could not be accomplished in two to three visits.

It really wasn't an unguarded moment but it certainly was serendipity that the La Jolla Marriott Hotel was a block away from the OrthoMed Center. As is the case of all modern hotels, they had an exercise center. It was a fairly well-equipped exercise center, which included both an indoor and outdoor pool (after all, it's Southern California!). This facility served as an amenity for the hotel guests.

In that we had an excess of exercise equipment, it was an easy proposition to contact the hotel management and suggest the following. If they would allow us to move in our exercise equipment and bring members of our staff to do the training, we would split the profits of this new fitness club—if they didn't charge us rent. We thought it was a rather exciting idea and even offered the hotel people additional business in the form of a physician-directed exercise program for chronic musculoskeletal disabilities. Although we weren't aware of any other hotel that was carrying out such a program, it seemed a good idea. To try to convey the positive aspects of this health club, we called it the Wellstrong Center.

Of course, not all the patients agreed that it was a good idea. Many, having paid for their health insurance or being covered by Medicare, felt that this extension of the training program that they had started in the OrthoMed Center should also be covered by health insurance. Perhaps ten to fifteen percent of the clientele at the OrthoMed Center could appreciate the progressive exercise program with appropriate equipment had to be funded out of pocket. It was more valuable than short-term pain relief, which they could get at any physical therapy center. Actually, we were surprised at the relatively small percentage who did decide to pursue continuing their exercise training on the same equipment but out of pocket. The American healthcare system has created a strong sense of entitlement. This is especially true of the older population, who enjoy the extensive benefits of Medicare. Many of the younger people, who had insurance policies which only covered catastrophic events, did take advantage of the training program.

Because the OrthoMed Center was a clinical practice office for about eight orthopaedic surgeons, the volume of people transferring to the Wellstrong program was significant and the program was financially successful. That success continued until the politics of the Orthopaedic Department changed and Scott and I both left the University. More about that later.

13

Workers' Compensation—Entitlement Versus Responsibility

In the previous chapter, the subject of entitlement was briefly discussed. This, of course, is a major issue for all governments, and certainly in American politics. It amounts to the transition of taxes into social support on many levels—Social Security, Medicare, etc. Historically, one of the first areas where this concept matched the entitlement of benefits to the individual based on broad taxation of many was in workers' compensation.

The need for this entitlement was certainly evident. With the industrial age, more and more injuries occurred from the unguarded moment of workers losing their limbs and perhaps their lives to a relentless machine, railroad accidents, explosions of steam engines, falling from heights in the workplace, on and on and on. These were not problems in the simple agrarian life before the industrial age. However, with the event of the maimed worker and certainly with the fatal injury, usually a widow and destitute family were created. In response to this, governments gradually passed legislation partially to reimburse the injured party or their family for the industrial accident. Initially, it was to reimburse them just for the lost wages but later it included medical expenses. Actually, in 1896, Germany was the first country to pass workers' compensation laws under Bismarck.

He did this as a political ploy in order to gain public support for many other policies being implemented.

In each state of the United States, slightly different rules for workers' compensation were passed by state legislatures up to 1912, when Mississippi was the last to initiate these rules. Actually, that's currently a bit of a problem in the United States in that each state has variations in the rules of payment for disability, mechanisms to identify disability and the amount of medical care to be provided. This has developed into a political football in that, by manipulation of the rules in each state, the injured worker can later become a candidate for Social Security Disability Insurance (SSDI), the federal safety net for disability for a worker of such a severity that work is not available. The sooner the state can transfer responsibility to the Federal systems such as SSDI, the better the economics for the businesses of the state.

But what does this have to do with therapeutic exercise? Actually, quite a lot. What follows is a discussion of how a very worthy concept, financial help for the injured worker, has turned into a very unsavory industry which overall has little regard for that injured worker. And, as you'll see, the point of this discussion from my biased view is that much of the abuse of the system by attorneys, employers, injured workers, politicians and physicians could be resolved by the use of progressive resistive exercise. What a concept!

Earlier, I discussed the California Industrial Medical Council. As described then, it was created in order to avoid the excesses and abuse of the California workers' compensation system. Because the award of disability was largely made on the basis of description of pain, the amount of disability an injured worker manifests is open to considerable argument. There is no practical way to measure pain.

To try and find some alternative to this wasteful system of disability award, the California legislature, in 1995, asked the Industrial Medical Council to "investigate the feasibility of using objective medical findings to identify the severity of soft tissue injures." That was the wording of the legislation. It sounds pretty simple. On the other hand, what are objective medical findings? For some medical problems, that's also pretty simple. For high blood pressure, the measurement of the systolic and diastolic pressure is an objective medical finding. For a fracture, the X-ray demonstrating the location and alignment of the fracture is an objective medical finding. Well, how about the pain associated with repetitive workplace activity such as continuous computer work? In the jargon of the workers' compensation system, this is known as "continuous trauma". More than that, how about neck pain after an auto accident or back pain after frequent lifting? What are the objective medical findings?

The Search for Objective Medical Findings

The Industrial Medical Council requested bids from many research organizations to respond to the legislative request. Having been a past member of the Industrial Medical Council, I was aware of this opportunity and contacted Len Matheson, Ph.D., the psychologist with whom I had worked back in the Rancho days, to come up with a proposal. No one else bid on this project. Thus, the Orthopaedic Department at the University of California San Diego was awarded $75,000 to answer this request—to identify the feasibility of using objective medical findings to identify the severity of soft tissue injuries. By the arrangements of the contract, we had to give quarterly reports and the project had to be completed in a year.

The measurement of disability had been a longtime project for Dr. Matheson. He was familiar with the literature.

Thus, in the first quarterly report, we presented a survey of the current literature relative to the measurement of pain from over a thousand references. We gave objective evidence that there was no credible scientific methodology with which to measure pain. We thus proposed that the objective medical findings would have to be the measurement of function. Now, that's an interesting concept. Actually, relative to workers' compensation, it is an important concept. In that the disabled worker was receiving medical care and payments for the inability to work, the question of what functional limitations prevented the worker from returning to the workplace, at least in some manner, is important. Theoretically, the limitation in function is created by pain. Lacking a way to measure pain, the next best thing is to measure function. Well, that sounds reasonable but, how would you measure function? Len Matheson had been involved in this question for many years. He, indeed, had coined the word "work hardening" to describe focus at return to work by improved function by a rehabilitation program. In many areas, work-site reproduction was used as a method to identify whether the injured worker could return to the job. If the job was as a baggage handler, the rehabilitation center would have various sized suitcases and other baggage on which the worker would practice. If the job was as a telephone lineman, the center would have telephone poles to climb, etc. This turned out to be a very expensive and overall ineffective way to identify levels of disability.

Well, if you didn't try to reproduce the workplace, how could you measure a worker's capacity to return to the job? Really, it turns out that it's not that important to specifically identify whether a worker can do a specific job, but rather his/her overall capacity to function at similar activities in the workplace. Many years earlier, the Federal Department of Occupational Health had identified levels of disability,

228

specifically labeling the physical demands of a generic task and labeling them with adjectives. It was known as the "Physical Demand Characteristics". Thus, someone who was labeled as able to do "very heavy work" could lift over 100 pounds. Someone labeled as "heavy" could lift seventy-five pounds, "moderate" fifty pounds, etc. In terms of jobs that require manual lifting, these broad classifications in general were quite sufficient to identify work abilities.

To pursue this project to measure function, Dr. Matheson revised the earlier type of test, called psychophysical testing, with this person being evaluated was asked to lift progressively increasing weights to shelves, which generally correlated to knee level, waist level and shoulder level. Matheson modified it so that the amount of weight was unknown to the person being tested. He used milk crates in which various colored sandbags were placed. The therapist carrying out the test, of course, knew the weight of the sandbag by its color but, because each sandbag was exactly the same size, it was impossible for the evaluee to know the weight which the evaluator placed in the milk crate before it was lifted. Also, to make it more fair when comparing short people to tall people, the level of shelves could be varied to adjust to the evaluee's height. Finally, during the course of the test at various stages of the test, pulse rate was monitored. It's a physiologic reality that the more physical stress the individual is tolerating, the more the heart rate will increase. Those evaluees making a valid effort to demonstrate their capacity would have a gradual increase in heart rate, which would correlate with the amount of physical activity they were doing. The lifting of weights was in a standardized manner, lifting from floor to the various shelf heights in a slow, steady manner with the same amount of time between each lift. Those whose heart rate did not change obviously were not making a valid effort to comply with the test protocol.

A far more innovative maneuver was added to the test. This was called the "Spinal Function Short". This was a series of drawings depicting a man or woman carrying out normal physical activities such as bending down to plug a cord into a wall socket or pushing a wheelbarrow full of sand up an incline. The evaluee was asked to fill out on an answer sheet whether they could or could not do the activity being depicted. They could answer this on a scale of five, whether they were sure they could not versus whether they were sure they could. They also could state they didn't know. This was scored and correlated with the actual physical testing. We'll get to that later. There were several other characteristics to the test as well. The whole test was labeled the Cal FCP for "Functional Capacity Procedure".

A clinical study demonstrating the test was presented to the Industrial Medical Council at the appropriate time, less than one year after the awarding of the contract. However, the Industrial Medical Council did not recognize it as a valid response to the request for objective medical findings. In addition, it was not recognized as a test which the Industrial Medical Council could support because it used commercial equipment. The milk crates, sandbags and adjustable shelves were sold to the user. We felt it necessary that, for the test to be valid and comparable, all test equipment should be the same. Certainly, somebody has to manufacture a yardstick or a tape measure and sell them. We offered plans for all the materials if someone wished to manufacture them themselves. It would be costly. The basic reason for nonacceptance was that the applicant lawyers and the doctors on the Industrial Medical Council to whom they referred cases did not wish to come up with a mechanism. This could offer some objective information which might overpower a patient's exaggerated statement of pain so severe that they hurt too much to go back to work. Pain is a subjective complaint.

230

How Do We Control Entitlement Medical Costs?

This brings us into a discussion of workers' compensation and even Social Security disability and their relationship to an active exercise program as indicated at the beginning of this chapter.

Although on occasion serious injuries occur in the workplace, with increasing emphasis on workplace safety, the actual number of these injuries has decreased. Even the soft-tissue injuries have decreased in incidence. Yet, the cost of medical care and the duration of time off work has continued to increase. Why?

Can it be that the soft-tissue injuries are now more significant? Hardly. The workplace is by far safer in the last decade than in any before. But more than that, how bad do the injuries have to be to cause pain? As a marvelous example of how benign soft-tissue injuries can be, a study was done on demolition car drivers. These crazy people receive an average of sixty impacts a night as the derby proceeds, wherein one car rams another in an effort to disable it. Although there is some neck pain the following day, long-term residual whiplash in these drivers has never been reported. Or take the pilots who have been ejected from planes in training accidents. The force of ejection is so severe that there is a twenty percent incidence of compression fractures of the spine as the pilot is shot out of the dying plane's cockpit. Long-term whiplash has never been reported in this group of competitive people.

Well, what is the cause of prolonged disability from soft-tissue injury such as whiplash or lumbar strain? Some of it has to do with this idea of entitlement. Due to the event happening at work, this is transferred to being the fault of the company—not due to just an accident or even clumsiness, which would be the cause of the same accident had it occurred at home on the weekend. The boss is responsible for me now. I am entitled to be 100 percent before I go back to work. This is especially true if the worker doesn't like the job or the boss.

And then there's litigation. In California, the attorney gets more money the longer the case is prolonged and the higher the cost of medical care. He is working on percentages. Thus, it is quite reasonable for the attorney to encourage surgical care with its associated costs and delays in recovery over nonoperative care. The nonoperative care which is encouraged is merely passive care, which reduces the pain temporarily. This is in the form of modalities such a ultrasound, heat and cold packs, massage, electrical stimulation, etc. No scientific study has ever demonstrated that these maneuvers were of benefit for healing. The only mechanism where soft-tissue healing can be created is by an active progressive exercise program.

When a really expensive worker (a professional athlete) is injured, they are not sent for a home exercise program, not sent for adjustment or massage, not sent to have hot packs and cold packs—they are sent to the athletic trainer employed by the professional organization. The athletic trainer takes them to the training room, which is at the headquarters of every professional team, and puts them through training exercises—many of them on specialized equipment. This is nearly an unknown event to the nonprofesional athlete, the injured industrial worker. They do get mechanisms to relieve their acute pain—and this is justified in the early days and weeks following an injury. However, they are not progressed, as the professional athlete is, to an active progressive resistance exercise program.

That's the premise of this whole book. An active, progressive exercise program could salvage many injuries and degenerative problems, especially if carried out early in the healing process. A nice documentation of this phenomenon occurred in the state of Utah. Dr. Alan College is the medical director of the Labor Commission, which supervises health-care for the injured worker in Utah. In 1997, he changed the regulations for physical therapy. One could not get repeat visits to physical therapy as an injured worker unless the physical therapist demonstrated some improvement in function. Merely making that regulation brought the number of physical therapy visits down from sixteen to twelve on average. It decreased the use of hot packs fifty percent and increased the use of active exercises forty-five percent. Just focusing at function rather than control of pain was enough to change physical therapy treatment plans.

Because Dr. College is a practicing occupational health physician, who started out as a carpenter, then became a physical therapist and then a general practitioner before his current role, he understood the benefits of early return to work. Indeed, it is well-documented that absence from work is detrimental to your health. In one of the most dramatic studies reported in 2001 by Dr. Nylen and Floderus, a review of work status of twins in Sweden was carried out. Because of the important medical information available as to the genetic aspect of disease, in Sweden as well as in Finland, all twins are registered and their medical status is recorded. This study noted the mortality of 2,500 women and 11,000 men from 1973 to 1996. Their employment status was also noted. The unemployed man was nearly twice as likely to die earlier than his employed twin. The unemployed woman was fifty percent more likely to die earlier than the employed woman, even when controlled for potential social, behavioral, work and health-related confounders. The value of work as a health benefit, however, is seldom a point of interest to the injured worker, his attorney or even his doctor.

The medical profession has a great burden in the care of the injured worker. There is the worker's lack of motivation to return to an unhappy job. With the desire to prolong the problem and make it as costly as possible from the attorney, the orthopaedic surgeon is quite pleased to pursue and be highly reimbursed for surgical care which has limited potential to be successful. This is certainly the case for lumbar fusions. In a recent study from Sweden, discussed briefly earlier, comparing three different techniques for lumbar fusion done for back pain, it was found that the various techniques made no difference in the effectiveness. Even though these were well-selected, only one-third of the operated patients went back to work. Several recent studies have shown that, with an active exercise program, the chances of getting a good result and return to work are as good as a lumbar fusion with no complication or reoperation. There were numerous complications in the surgical group. One study is from Sweden as well and another with similar results is from England. Such a study is highly unlikely to be done in the United States due to the belief system of all spinal surgeons that fusion surgery is effective. A few surgeons, like Dr. Carragee at Stanford University, are willing to look at it in a scientific manner. This surgeon compared one specific procedure—an anterior interbody fusion done for a specific diagnosis which causes back pain due to instability, spondylolisthesis—to another group of patients with back pain secondary to degeneration of the disc and positive discograms. There was an eighty percent success rate in the spondylolisthesis patients and a twenty percent success rate in the back patients due to degeneration, doing exactly the same type surgery.

Regrettably, I could supply patient history after patient history as to how surgery done inappropriately on psychologically disabled individuals has left them with ruined lives.

There is a specific reimbursable medical diagnosis called "failed back syndrome". This has never been applied to patients carrying out a nonoperative treatment program. It is just used for postsurgery patients.

What can be done for this problem? It is a large problem. The cost of Social Security disability is about $22 billion annually. $19 billion is secondary to financial awards for injuries. The great majority of these injuries are not the usual catastrophic spinal cord injury/brain trauma problems. They are for ordinary back pain and neck pain secondary to degenerative changes and many of them secondary to failed surgery. It is for this reason that this whole discussion about a mundane problem such as active progressive exercise as a treatment for spinal and extremity injuries is important. This has been the story of how I found out it was important. Unfortunately, this is not a bit of knowledge which is typical for orthopaedic surgeons or the medical profession as a whole. In the year of this writing, 2005, I attended the annual meeting of the American Academy of Orthopaedic Surgeons. There were about 700 presentations. None of the presentations were focused at rational nonoperative care of any type. None were focused at the obscene costs of surgery and failed surgery. Chronic back pain is a mundane problem but terribly important for its social and financial issues. Why?

14

How Did It Get So Screwed Up?

The last word in the previous chapter was "why", referring essentially to the lack of interest of orthopedic surgery is nonoperative care. The "it" in the title of this chapter also refers to nonoperative care for what I have been calling mundane ailments. By this I mean back pain, post whiplash pain, carpal tunnel syndrome, degenerative arthritis and soft-tissue strain. Of course, these ailments are not mundane to the person suffering from them but, on the scale of things that are medically serious, such as malignancies, fractures, infections, etc., they are less serious. They are mundane in that they are seldom fatal unless there are complications with surgery. What, then, are the forces competing against rational nonoperative care?

Education

This has been a story of my education as to the role of exercise as an active treatment for the "mundane ailments". This story has taken us through some of the education of an orthopedic surgeon and some of the history of orthopedics. We have discussed the development of rehabilitation as an organized treatment program. Also, we discussed some of the history behind the various contributing factors in nonoperative care, such as osteopathy, chiropractic, physical

236

therapy and exercise science. All of these have filled a need but, while these various entities were developing, medical schools were developing large research sections as has the pharmacologic industry. These resulted in many breakthroughs in treatment of serious disorders. Certainly, a better understanding of the causes for cancer and infection has developed. In addition, the industry of surgical implants has developed many technically clever devices to assist in surgery, creating artificial joints and, with the marvels of optics and micro-video, allowing anthroscopic surgery and other minimally invasive surgical procedures to prosper.

To gain a scientific understanding of the mechanisms of disease, the physiology of the organism and, especially in the context of our current discussion, the neuromuscular system, a considerable amount of time of medical school teaching is necessary. Moreover, the technology and technique of surgery is not simple and it takes many years for competence to emerge with this craft. By and large, medical school is focused at the understanding and treatment of serious disease. Moreover, medical doctors are not taught much about physical nonoperative methods of care. The osteopaths do have courses in manipulation but because the mechanisms of benefit are poorly understood and many competing alternative systems of therapy are available which require less skill and charisma, that form of treatment is being downgraded, even in the osteopathic schools. The chiropractors continue to prosper with the craft of manipulation and do offer a high level of initial success for the aches and pains but do not expect or even wish to achieve curative mechanisms of care. Maintenance chiropractic is still a favored view of care among many. Thus, there is little time for interest in teaching the mundane physical treatments in medical school.

The reader may think I am overstating the case but the evidence is clear. When I was Chairman of Orthopedic Surgery at the University of Texas Southwestern in Dallas, there was a block of time allocated for lectures to the medical school class. Given all the other competing areas of interest, the time was rather small so that it ended up that, in their entire four-year career, students only received a forty-five minute lecture on one occasion on back pain. From an overall expense standpoint, including costs of disability, back pain is the costliest ailment in modern society. There is a little imbalance!

The brief time, however, is understandable in one sense. Actually, from a scientific standpoint, we still don't understand the basic causes of back pain. Even with the sophisticated MRI, which depicts the soft tissues of the spine with excellent precision, one cannot tell which disc is painful, even if degenerated. Twenty percent of normal populations have herniated discs which would appear in need of operation except that the individual has no pain. Why a lumbar disc can herniate one day when the individual just bends over to tie his shoe is still an enigma. Lacking an understanding of the cause, from a scientific standpoint, it is very difficult to come up with a rational treatment. Progress is being made to understand the abnormal chemistry that emerges in a painful disc but we still don't know why some discs develop this abnormal chemistry. There remains a huge area of ignorance. The doctors still have to treat the symptoms without understanding the cause. It is somewhat like treating a fever with ice to the forehead without understanding the bacteria, which is the source of the fever. There is, at this point, no specific pharmacologic agent for back pain.

Pharmaceutical Profits

Let's look at the pharmacologic industry. It is not news that they are one of the most profitable industries in America. One phase of this is the extensive advertising, both directly to doctors and to the public as a whole. This has created a need for more and more pharmacologic alternatives. They have created the presumption that pain is a disease which can be stamped out with enough pills. Recently, some of the extensive advertising has backfired in the form of the COX-2 inhibitors—like Vioxx and Bextra. Although extensive preliminary research went into the development of these agents, some of the data was ignored in the preliminary phases of development and it turns out there is a higher incidence of heart disease and stroke with these anti-inflammatory medications. Some of this is due to selective publication of results. Although many studies are funded, not all are necessarily published. When a researcher receives money from a drug firm, he/she also agrees that the results will be published after review by the funding company. Sometimes the pharmaceutical companies just shelve the research which is not entirely favorable.

There is a move afoot by the various high-level publications, such as the *Journal of the American Medical Association* and the *New England Journal of Medicine,* that all research funded by anybody be registered. The results of that research will then necessarily be made visible in some form to the experts in the field so that poor results cannot be hidden.

This is not just a problem of a few complications among hundreds of episodes of safe use. The fastest form of addiction is to prescription drugs. The worst is a product known as oxycodone, which can be provided as long-acting narcotic. All the drugs used in America are described in significant detail in a book which comes out annually, known as the *Physician's Desk Reference (PDR)*. In the description of oxycodone, it is stated that it has an addiction capabillity similar to morphine. Later on in the discussion (all the drug descriptions are written by the manufacturers), it states it is appropriate for "moderate to severe pain". That means it can be prescribed for back pain. No one would ever prescribe morphine for ordinary back pain.

Because of its relative ease of accessibility as a prescription drug, it rapidly flows into the illicit drug culture. It's easy to get from Mexico and Canada as well. Unfortunately, it's more expensive than heroin and so, once an individual gets hooked on this drug, it's cheaper to shift into more reasonable recreational drugs. Deaths from overdose of oxycodone have risen fivefold since 1997 in Utah. Emergency Room visits in Utah due to prescription drug complications have risen threefold for adolescents. Yet, this drug is being extensively marketed to physicians for all sorts of pain problems.

It's easy to see how a busy physician would rather write a prescription for either an anti-inflammatory or a pain pill than to take the time to describe the benefits of an active exercise program. All of us are lazy. Patients don't like the sound that they are going to have to make a significant effort to help themselves. They would rather have hot packs, massage, etc. To counterbalance that with the facts that only exercise can change tissue and guide healing takes time and certainly a belief system on the part of the physician that it really is of benefit. As noted above, most physicians have not been trained that exercise is a therapeutic tool other than in a general sense. The specifics of an exercise program have never been described to the doctor and patients are usually referred to the physical therapists. Physical therapists, on the other hand, get paid more for passive care than an active exercise program. They seldom make the effort to proceed into an instruction as to the value of exercise. Thus, little support comes from either the physicians or the allied health community.

The Business of Surgery

And let's look at surgery. The instrument makers have a history quite parallel to the pharmacologic industry. What started out as small companies with expert machinists have burgeoned into a huge industry, again one of the most profitable in America. Just as the pharmacologic manufacturer have become very competitive due to the luscious profits in the industry, the same is true of the manufacturers of surgical implants and the equipment to carry out the surgery. A good example of this is the total hip industry. The design of the total hip replacement at first glance is relatively simple. One needs to reproduce the ball and socket joint, which is the anatomy of the human hip. However, the various materials for the bearing surfaces can vary a lot. Now we have ceramic, metal and plastic systems. In addition, the design of the stem and the cup which replaces the acetabulum have a great number of variations and methods of implanting them. There are over 150 designs for a total hip. The same is true for total knees. Each design is extensively marketed in the journals and one reason there are so many medical journals is that here, too, it's a profitable business with a wide number of advertisers in the form of the pharmacologic companies and the implant makers. There are far more medical journals than any physician can digest. There are journals which are summary articles of other journal articles and then what are known as "throwaway journals", which are summaries of summaries. Often these are written by a scientific writer whose pay is somewhat dependent upon the advertising from various manufacturers. There is a wonderful opportunity to selective presentation of facts.

One is beginning to see advertising to the public as to the appropriate total knee or total hip replacement. Of course, that's crazy. There is no way that a non-expert can identify what particular replacement is appropriate for them. When even highly experienced expert surgeons can't agree on the various nuances of design and materials, it's obscene to think that the public can have a reasonable opinion. But the role of advertising is to create a specific appetite. The industrial profits demonstrate that it works.

And then there is the total disc replacement. This is just now emerging as a potential to replace spinal fusions. That would seem to be not a bad idea in that that's the natural history which occurred with our other joints. Before the development of total joint replacements, the usual solution for a damaged knee, hip or ankle was a fusion to stop motion completely. It would create a painless joint but naturally would stress the other joints and often created premature breakdown there. Thus, when a viable total joint replacement emerged, it was a solution to many problems. It is not clear whether that's the case with the total disc replacement. There is a whole series of other problems in the spine which are more complex than merely joint replacement for hip or knee. The track record for success of fusions, even when technically perfect and the fusion was solid, offers overall only fifty percent improvement and, on average, only a third go back to work. No one truly understands those dismal statistics, which certainly are far worse than total knee and total hip results. As described earlier, there are many factors in back pain which are not simple mechanical abnormalities. Many of the patients with fusions or total discs could have avoided surgery with appropriate exercises.

The Role of the Insurance Companies

And yet there is another factor which retards the use of an active exercise program for the nonoperative care of musculoskeletal problems. This is the insurance industry. Take the case of a patient I recently evaluated. She was a sixty-year-old lady who was delivering some business mail for her employer at the local post office. While waiting to move into a parking slot just being vacated by another car, a third car was backing out of a parking slot. The driver, not recognizing the waiting car, backed into the driver's side door of her car. Apparently my patient's car was in the blind spot of the backing driver. Actually, it was quite a minor hit. Her car was drivable. After the usual exchange of information and apologies, my patient drove to the local Emergency Room for evaluation. She had had a past history of two spine surgeries, one of which was a fusion ten years earlier, but had no particular back problems. At the same time of the accident, she did not have any particular pain other than some neck strain. X-rays were taken at the Emergency Room and she was released. Over the next several days, however, she began developing more back pain. She got a lawyer and was referred to a doctor, who evaluated her and started her on physical therapy of the "fake and bake" characteristic. She continued to get worse. It is a long and tortuous story and I won't go into all details but what follows is that, about two years later, she had a spine fusion with a fusion at the segment above the previous surgery.

Because of the use of her forearms to get up from a seated position due to the back pain, she developed pain in her shoulders and had reconstructive surgery to both shoulders. Because of the pressure on the hands she pushed up, she developed bilateral carpal tunnel syndrome and had surgical release of both wrists. Because of some weakness of the leg which developed after the surgery, one day her leg gave out and she fell on her knee, developing pain in a knee which was already arthritic but not painful, and had an additional surgery.

Whose fault is it? She was working at the time of the injury and the insurance company for her employer denies liability for all of the problems. They could not be responsible for the problems from the minor soft-tissue injury of the accident. On the other hand, her attorney notes that she would not have developed these problems if she had not had the accident and thus the accident is the total cause. The insurance company of the employer made no attempt to monitor or guide therapy and the tests.

From my view, she would not have required any surgery at all if she had had appropriate nonoperative care with an active exercise program following a soft-tissue strain. That would be the rational treatment provided to an athlete. No professional team exists without their athletic trainer and training room with assorted exercise equipment. That would have resolved her problem in the early stages. None of the treating surgeons had tried any sort of active exercise program but, recognizing abnormalities seen on the MRI and noting her gradually increasing pain complaints, proceeded with various surgical procedures to try to address the preinjury, asymptomatic degenerative changes seen on the MRI. Oh, in addition to all of the surgery, because of her inability to work, she developed emotional problems. She was a widow with poor social support in the community. She then started seeing a psychiatrist and was placed on numerous drugs as well. It is now five years since the minor accident. She has been unable to return to any form of work since. The case goes to court in about six months. Whose fault is it?

Certainly, the surgeons get compensated more for the surgical procedures than for referring her to an active exercise program. The attorney lives on the length of disability and the amount of medical bills. The attorneys for the employer's workers' compensation insurance company maintain employment because of the applicant's attorney, and are in no great haste to resolve the problem either. The workers' compensation insurance company does not have much urgency to create a more rational treatment system in that they merely raise the rates to achieve profitability. Everybody's feeding at the trough. No wonder the surgeons see workers' compensation as a pot of gold.

What can we do about it?

15

What Can We Do About It?

The "we" in the title is certainly the most important word. No idea can prosper without a consensus. As described in the beginning of this book, this is a tale about my own progressive understanding of an important but mostly unused component of general healthcare—active resistance exercise programs. I felt its role in modern life would be more effectively displayed when it became personalized by my own educational process. It certainly wasn't my idea. Rehabilitation in the general sense has been a progressive process, gaining strength over the years. It has gained more credibility when a society becomes more affluent and there is enough funding to care for longstanding chronic problems such as spinal cord injury and stroke. However, the credit for placing active resistance exercises into a system goes to Arthur Jones. He created the health club industry, which has persuaded people to work out. He deserves more accolades than merely a chapter in this book. But, as suggested above, the project takes a lot of people to make it work and, more importantly, a lot more to understand it and value its place in the healthcare world. By now, the reader must be turning over in his/her mind: *All this stuff about resistance exercise? That's such a minor thing. Why place it on a pedestal of being part of the healthcare system?* I'll give you a couple of examples.

The Scoliosis Story

Perhaps the most dramatic demonstration of therapeutic resistance exercises, but affecting only a very small number of people, is the treatment of adolescent scoliosis. The problem is frequently called idiopathic scoliosis, which means the cause is unknown. In spite of hundreds of investigations searching for abnormalities in young people who develop curvature of their spines during their growing years, no clear-cut cause has ever been identified. There are some genetic tendencies, but only a weak association. There are some minor, very subtle neurologic variations such as with balance, emanating from the inner ear, but that testing is an unreliable predictor. The problem emerges painlessly, 8:1 in adolescent girls compared to boys. One factor is that the growth spurt of adolescents is usually quite short in girls, lasting only about two years in the early teens, while growth in boys may persist throughout their teenage years. The traditional treatment for adolescent scoliosis is surgery after failed bracing if the curvature gets too severe. This is usually figured at about forty-five degrees on a standing X-ray. At this age, our spines are very flexible and do vary somewhat in height between standing and recumbent, especially if there is a minor curvature. The surgical benefits have become progressively more significant with improved systems of fixing the thoracic and lumbar spine with metal rods and screws. The results nowadays are excellent except for the months taken to get over this very extensive surgery and the minor risk of infection and other complications. Deterioration of remaining, unfused segments may occur later in life.

Bracing for scoliosis is another thing. To be most effective, the braces have to be worn about twenty-three hours a day. The braces are form-hugging, plastic devices, trying to hold the spine in its normal, straight position. Compliance with wearing the braces is a difficult problem, however. Just at a time when a kid wants to be most like her tribe, wearing the styles of the times, etc., she is asked to wear this bulky brace to school and receive the derision of her friends. It's a tough job convincing teenagers, especially girls, to wear the brace for many months. The same, to a slightly lesser degree, goes for the boys. In the long run, on some occasions, the brace has not succeeded in stemming the tide of increasing curvature and, after a year wearing the brace, the child is told they'll have to have surgery anyway. There are several studies which question whether the braces ultimately affect the natural history at all.

Often, when the brace is discarded, the curvature returns to a greater degree. Some articles argue, if nothing had been done, the same curvature would have resulted at growth maturity. The relatively small curves don't increase after growth has been completed. Thus, many parents are told just to watch and wait and see if the curve increases and then await surgery when needed. This is unhappy advice to the parent who has just had the child's teeth straightened with months of bracing (much more easily accepted by adolescents since so many have it done and it's almost a rite of passage). At that point in time, many parents fall for the chiropractor's opinion that manipulations can stop the curve progression. This in spite of the evidence that no scientific paper has ever been presented documenting the benefit of chiropractic care in adolescent scoliosis. Success to a certain extent can be claimed, however, if the chiropractic care matches natural history when the progression of curve stops short of the surgically eligible curves. In a scientific sense, there is no way to predict which child will progress and which child will have the curve stop short of surgical need. It is true that, the earlier the scoliosis is identified, the greater the expectation for increase in curvature as she/he grows.

Wouldn't just usual exercise be of benefit in treating adolescent scoliosis? Actually, there are several scientific studies questioning that, and the findings were that exercise did not alter the rate of curvature change. Many avid swimmers, even at a championship level, have had their scoliotic curves increase. One would think such an exercise as swimming, where certainly the torso muscles are well-utilized, would be effective. It's not. Thus, I was taught and I taught my residents not to expect exercise to make any difference. Certainly, exercise for young people is important for health but the evidence up to now was that general exercise was not of benefit for treatment of idiopathic scoliosis.

And then another unguarded moment happened. As described earlier, we started a physical therapy program as part of the Department of Orthopaedic Surgery at UCSD. One of the pieces of equipment which Arthur had donated to the university was a torso rotation machine, which could accurately measure the force used by the torso in rotating in one direction or the other with the pelvis stabilized so that all the rotation force was coming from the torso musculature. It measured isometric strength of ten-degree increments in the full arc of torso rotation. Using this piece of equipment, some of our therapists discovered that young adolescents with scoliosis had an unequal strength when rotating in one direction compared to the other. This was new information. In some, it was weakness on rotating to the right. In some, it was weakness on rotating to the left. Nonetheless, it was a consistent finding.

We tested other adolescents and young adults, including the staff members, and found that everybody was about to equal in their strength to rotate from left to right and right to left. We decided therefore to try to see if we could balance the strengths of the adolescent scoliotics. Using a progressive exercise regimen twice a week on the same equipment which stabilized the pelvis and measured the resistance, the strengths became equal within several weeks of gradual increase of resistance. We also did EMG analysis by surface electrode and found that the lumbar paraspinal muscles were not very active at the beginning of the exercise. However, after the progressive exercise, they were quite normal when compared to individuals without scoliosis. These scoliosis patients were being monitored for their curvature by X-rays.

We soon discovered that no patients who participated in the strengthening program, and had a curve that was less than forty-five degrees, increased the curvature. In fact, eighty percent of them decreased their curvature by two to twenty percent. Their parents noted that they tended to stand straighter as well. We never could figure out how to measure this. Our results were published in two different journals, *The Journal of Spinal Disorders* and the journal, *Orthopaedics*. To our knowledge, this is the most successful non-operative treatment program for scoliosis ever published.

In order to gain more numbers of patients to treat, I sent a brochure to all of the surgeons in the San Diego area who were doing adolescent scoliosis care. As in any city, that's a relatively small number because this has now become a very specialized craft. I also indicated that the treatment would be complimentary. Since it was common knowledge that exercise would not benefit, insurance companies would not pay for it. They seldom pay for any form of therapeutic exercise. They would pay for the specialized braces for scoliosis, however.

In spite of the fact that the treatment was free and there was evidence to support its benefit, no surgeon has referred a patient for care. The patients appear largely by word of mouth.

There was the problem of gaining acceptance for a simple but, at the time, unconventional form of treatment. Getting my fellow surgeons to understand that this was "different" exercise has been almost impossible. The reason that exercise on specialized equipment was more effective than swimming is that the equipment isolated the inhibited muscles. The muscles were forced to work. No set of muscles could substitute for them. In so doing, the nervous system was retrained. That is an aspect of neuromotor training which had not been described in their physiology textbooks and lectures. Also, the value of feedback provided by a piece of equipment was not understood. If one carries out a calisthenics type of exercise program, there are so many modes of "cheating" so that it's very difficult to truly measure the amount of exercise and compare it to the exercise done on a previous occasion.

While exercising on a piece of equipment, there is no escape from the definable range, number of repetitions and the amount of resistance. Thus, it's clear to everyone involved, especially the exerciser, the amount of accomplishment on each occasion. Keeping a record of each day's level of activity allows a gradual progression. That, of course, is the key to effective neuromuscular training and progress. In our experience with the scoliotic adolescents, compliance was never a problem. The exercise only took about ten minutes, twice a week at first and later once a week. Compared to wearing a brace twenty-three hours a day—no problem. Yet, trying to communicate those obvious benefits to the medical community has been extremely difficult. The idea is too different, too simple, too cheap. Incidentally, the torso-strengthening exercise machine now used in our studies costs about the same as two custom-made scoliotic braces.

Chronic Back Pain Treatment

But that's for a very small number of patients. Can this exercise equipment-oriented, resistive exercise program be applied to more significant numbers? The most costly musculoskeletal ailment is chronic back pain. Back pain is the second most frequent source of doctor visits, upper respiratory infections being the first. That's a large enough number of patients on which to make an impact. In 1995, an orthopaedic surgeon in Minneapolis, Brian Nelson, published a paper in *Orthopaedics* concerning 627 chronic back pain patients treated with a progressive resistance exercise program. About seventy-five percent of this group had a good or excellent result which was maintained at ninety-four percent of the patients at one year follow-up. He followed a control group who were denied access to the resistive exercise program because their insurance companies did not feel it was of benefit. In those receiving the exercise training, on average the patients had tried and failed six different types of treatment programs before. Eighty-nine percent of the successful patients previously failed a program which was described as "exercise". The results were similar for varied diagnoses such as mechanical strain, degenerative disc disease, lumbar disc syndrome and spondylolisthesis. Thus, the diagnosis made no difference as to the treatment protocol. Reutilization of the healthcare system for back trouble within a year was thirteen percent. However, the group in which insurance failed to cover the active resistive exercise program had a forty-two percent reutilization of the healthcare system.

The specific point of this study showed that a home exercise program or use of health clubs with insufficient supervision could not be an effective treatment. Almost all the patients had tried low tech exercises and failed. Many of these chronic low back patients had pain which was exacerbated by their own medical care. By encouraging passive modalities, such as massage, heat and cold, the patients were made dependent on the healthcare system for a limitless stream of "feel good" treatments. This study, as many others, has shown that an active resistance exercise program which measures progress can give appropriate feedback as to improvement in objective terms. Rather than the fleeting feeling of benefit after the treatment is over, patients can document their improvement and demonstrate to themselves that they are getting better.

From the same group in Minneapolis, they studied a smaller group that had physician recommendation for surgery, many of whom had already been scheduled for the surgical care. However, after pursuing the exercise program, only 8.5 percent needed surgery. The cost savings were staggering. It was estimated that the cost of surgery in the presurgery group would have been $4.4 million, wherein the actual cost for the group being treated with resistance exercises was $400,000. Here again, the various diagnostic labels made no difference as to the outcomes.

A theoretic advantage of exercise equipment is that treatment to a significant extent is not based on the charisma or analytical skills of the therapist. If a standard protocol is used and appropriate precautions are taken, the personalities of the therapists should be rather irrelevant to the results. This hypothesis was challenged by another study which we carried out here in San Diego. In this study, 412 patients were treated at two separate centers, one at the UCSD Physical Therapy Center and the other at Physicians' Neck and Back Clinic in Minneapolis, Minnesota. 310 were treated in the San Diego Clinic and 102 in the Minneapolis Clinic. They all had the same evaluation scheme, which is a well-accepted question and answer test for health status, known as the SF-36 (short form-36). They all had a one-year follow-up. All patients had chronic low back pain and failed several previous forms of treatment.

The San Diego group included eleven percent who failed surgery and the Minneapolis group had fourteen percent who had failed surgery. Overall, seventy-five percent of the Minneapolis group and eighty-two percent of the San Diego group reported that they were considerably better as confirmed by their SF-36 scores and statements as to pain status. There was significant improvement in range and strength in all of those improved. Here, again, reuse of the healthcare system was low at ten percent at one year in the San Diego group and carried out in North Carolina, which did not have an active exercise component in their care, showed that there was a seventy-three percent reutilization of the healthcare system within a year.

In the Minneapolis group, the therapists were all physical therapists, while most of the therapists in the San Diego group were exercise physiologists. The study showed that the particular flavor of the therapist was not important, but the protocols, based on progress on specialized equipment, were important with resultant very similar results in two different centers that obviously had two different personalities of treaters. At both centers, only about four percent got worse and these became surgical candidates. Certainly, these studies demonstrated a significant advantage of progressive exercise on specialized equipment. This was published in the journal *Spine* in 1999.

There are additional studies in the medical literature documenting the benefit of specialized exercises for osteoporosis, sacroiliac problems and even back pain associated with pregnancy. Even though the articles have been published, this simple, uncomplicated and very safe approach has not been widely accepted. There are so many competing voices, shouting their benefit.

How Do You Measure Benefit?

Nonetheless, recognizing the value of progressive exercises on equipment, Scott Leggett and I formed a company to develop treatment programs on this line. The company was named "Measurement Driven Rehabilitation System" (MDRS) to emphasize the specific goal of progressing treatment on the basis of objective findings. One segment of the company was focused at developing physical therapy centers which were identified by the company label as "Spine & Sport Centers". Currently, the company owns or manages twelve centers in California and Idaho. It has been financially successful with plans for continued growth.

The value of the measurement-driven characteristics of the PT companies is emphasized due to recent change in regulations in California. California had an extremely wasteful workers' compensation payment system, whose costs were twice the U.S. average. Yet, in spite of that, the benefits to the worker were among the lowest in the United States. Such a system was crying out for reforms. As part of the reform movement which swept Arnold Schwarzenegger into office (known as the "Governator" as resonance from his movie roles in the *Terminator* series) during the recall election of the previous governor, workers' compensation reforms were accepted. One of these reforms was a limit of twenty-four physical therapy visits for workers' compensation patients. This was unfortunate for a referral therapy center, often treating chronic patients and surgical failures, such as our Spine & Sport Centers. Most of the patients already have had a lot of physical therapy prior to being referred to our centers. However, on the basis of documentation that we could demonstrate improvement by various test maneuvers, continued care has been accepted by the insurance companies. This is in contrast to many of our physical therapy competitors, who cannot muster a justification for continued care and have had to greatly reduce the size of their operations.

Here, again, the unguarded moment event was important. In a previous chapter, I described the role of Dr. Len Matheson in responding to the California request for using objective medical findings to document benefit of care. This was achieved by both a combination of physical testing and patient evaluation of their performance capacity based on drawings of common human activities. As noted in that discussion, this response to the legislature's request was not accepted by the California Industrial Medical Council in 1996, largely due to the fact that it did not account for pain. As noted at that time, pain was the decision point in California as to the amount of disability. All would agree, however, there is no objective measurement of pain. Exaggeration of pain had led to a lot of fraud in the system.

As another phase of MDRS, a research and education foundation was developed. A qualified director of research was hired. This turned out to be a chiropractor who, after five years of clinical work, decided that more objective analysis of musculoskeletal problems was necessary. He proceeded to achieve a Ph.D. in exercise science from Syracuse University. On this basis, we hired John Mayer, Ph.D., as research director of The Spine & Sport Foundation. Another chiropractor, Dr. Joe Verna, has been invaluable for our clinical research. He, too, was concerned about the lack of objective measurement in chiropractic care and volunteered for several months. He is now our Director of Operations at Spine & Sport Centers.

One of Dr. Mayer's projects was to utilize a computer to simplify the use of drawings as a method to identify level of disability. This was both for the lumbar spine as well as the extremities and cervical spine. The test, based on Matheson's Spinal Function Sort and Hand Function Sort, grew to 111 pictures and has been named the eMTAP (Multidimensional Task Ability Profile). We now use this test to identify baseline in performance and the amount of benefit following physical therapy. Papers have been published, documenting the very similar results achieved by this test using drawings when compared to actual physical testing. The test is used by several other centers and we plan to expand its use in a wider scope. We have used it to measure benefit of various current treatments. The justification for enthusiasm for such a test is that it simplifies the problem of identifying disability by measuring function. By the magic of the computer, various aspects of human performance can be identified and thus the weak links clarified for special interest in therapy. Because it is a computer model, the data is always complete and the math is always correct, in contrast to a pen and paper questionnaire type of test. If I hadn't had the opportunity to be on the California Industrial Medical Council, we never would have got the grant to develop the Cal FCP and ultimately have the scientific basis to develop the eMTAP.

How to Deliver Therapeutic Exercise to the Public

But still there are the costs of medical care. Also, the American people have been led to expect that unlimited medical care is a right rather than a privilege. Only a small percentage are willing to pay cash for healthcare treatment. This is a bit ironic, when one considers what is sometimes seen to be an exorbitant cost when things are broken in the household or in our cars. Nonetheless, the fee of a plumber or a mechanic is readily paid in that there is an obvious, immediate need which has to be fixed to allow normal life to go on. In healthcare, the immediacy of the solution is seldom so dramatic as a broken pipe. Nonetheless, the reality of the need is clearly evident as demonstrated by the several studies discussed above.

To try to respond to the fact that insurance companies, especially those not involved with workers' compensation, offer such poor coverage for therapeutic exercise, we had to develop an alternative. From the insurance company standpoint, the minimal coverage for acute as well as chronic problems is justified in that the benefits of physical therapy have seldom been demonstrated in any objective manner. All recognize that continued use of ultrasound, electrical stimulation, massage, hot packs, cold packs, can't do much to resolve a persistent musculoskeletal ailment which can be defined as a "weak link". Those treatments have never been demonstrated to improve the healing or strengthening process, yet are generally reimbursed by the insurance company.

To try and solve that problem while at the OrthoMed Center, Scott Leggett and I, with the help of some input from various therapists, dreamed up the idea of utilizing the health club at a nearby Marriott Hotel to develop a for-cash system. We called this center the "Wellstrong Center" to emphasize the two goals—increased strength and improved health, achieved through an active resistance exercise program. The Marriott Hotel in La Jolla agreed to this arrangement because their health club, as in most hotels, was merely an amenity and was not a revenue producing center. They agreed to allow us to move our equipment into the center and use our therapists. We would split the profits and they would not charge us rent. While Scott Leggett and I were at

UCSD, the project worked rather well. We sometimes would rotate the therapists from the formal physical therapy program to the Wellstrong Center so that they could gain insight. Certainly, individuals who are paying cash for their care are more avid and enthusiastic exercisers. They took pleasure in improvement as contrasted with some of their workers' compensation patients. The maneuver also avoided "therapist burnout".

After both Scott Leggett and I had left the University, the Wellstrong Center began to flounder. There was a lack of enthusiasm for the concept with the rest of the Orthopaedic Department at UCSD. They, like many orthopaedic surgeons, had developed little enthusiasm for an active, progressive resistance exercise program, especially protocol driven. This is in spite of the fact that there are many articles demonstrating the benefits of exercise for many common orthopedic ailments such as knee arthritis or rotator cuff problems. A paper published in 1995 by a well-known shoulder surgeon (Dr. Peterson) had demonstrated that 2/3 of the patients referred to him for repair of rotator cuff injuries could resolve their problems by an active, progressive exercise program to the shoulder. Exercises had just become a matter of diminished interest from the surgeon's standpoint. Control over physical therapy programs was not reimbursed.

It was apparent to us at the Spine & Sport Center that there were many patients who would benefit from continued exercise programs but had used up all the funding available from their various insurance policies. We therefore bought the rights to the Wellstrong program from the University and developed a new center, called "CORE Spinal Fitness". This was placed in a shopping center complex, which included a medical office building. This is a rather recent development in the various projects of MDRS. The CORE center shares space with a spine surgeon who has recognized the value of active exercises—Dr. Raiszadeh. We also are marketing to primary care doctors who have patients with the same dilemma of insufficient physical therapy healthcare coverage. As time passes, we hope to encourage other spine surgeons to incorporate CORE Spinal Fitness as a component of their complete package of healthcare delivery. Certainly, all spinal problems do not require surgery. Nonetheless, all surgeries do benefit from a progressive strengthening program. There is a significant niche for this type of program. Time will tell. Will the medical community and the population as a whole accept these concepts? This is the purpose of this book.

Thus, our personal solution of how we can fix it is to offer a varied menu of treatment programs, all offering an objective measurement of progress in the form of improved function, either of the extremities or the spine. Our marketing focus now is on primary care physicians, who are searching for solutions to musculoskeletal problems insufficiently resolved by medications. Primary care physicians are heavily marketed by the pharmaceutical industry but many things cannot be resolved by pills. What pill do you give a pregnant woman for back pain? What pill is available to correct the deformity of compression fractures associated with osteoporosis? Many patients will not accept anti-inflammatory medication taken forever as a solution to their back and joint aches. With the help of our research director and our measurement tool, the eMTAP test, we hope to document the benefit of appropriate treatment with measured resistance exercise.

I mentioned earlier the reforms that have occurred in California related to workers' compensation regulation. One of the regulations was that care be provided which was evidence-based. The standard for evidence-based care is a book put out by the Occupational Medicine Specialty, called *The*

American College of Occupational Medicine (ACOEM) Guidelines. In the multiple chapters, there is a consistent emphasis on improved function as a criteria of justification for continued care. Unfortunately, there are not many applications specifically reinforcing that intuitively correct concept. With the tools and concepts described above, however, we feel in a better position than most to fit into the changing aspects of medical care.

That is our solution. All in all, it is insignificant in the grand scale of American Medical Care. What will the future bring? We think it is significant in that this approach can significantly reduce need for surgery and long-term costs.

16

And Then the Future

Although I certainly plan to learn more, we have come to the end of this meandering tale of my education related to the role of resistance exercise. Earlier, I apologized for making such a big deal for what, after all, would seem to be a pretty simple, straightforward project—exercise for better health. The concept is certainly not news. Even though what type of diet is most appropriate, what medications are appropriate or even what surgery is appropriate changes as time passes, no scientific article has ever disregarded the benefits of progressive exercise.

Can a Demand for Measurement of Benefit Help?

The problem is in the relationship of physical therapy to therapeutic exercise. Mainstream medicine has not seen fit to measure the amount of exercise needed for musculoskeletal care. Medical literature usually does not report level of baseline function and concluding function after treatment. On the other hand, scientific papers concerning surgical fusion always speak about the status of the lumbar fusion at the time of evaluation, identified by X-ray. Treatment of infections is always identified by lab studies demonstrating resolution. But whether the exercise program being analyzed and compared to other treatments was considered of benefit or not, a statement of amount of progress seldom is defined. The reality is, unless one is using some means of exercise on a piece of equipment, one cannot accurately measure progress. One cannot identify the percentage of strength improvement or improvement in range of motion or number of repetitions. Literature regarding aerobic exercise and exercise for cardiac therapeutic function usually does have a report of baseline and amount of improvement. Regrettably, restorative exercise for the musculoskeletal system is thought to be too mundane to be concerned, and is usually classified as "conservative care failed" or "conservative care helped".

Will that ever change?

It will only change if funding agencies demand some documentation of benefit before additional care is provided. That has not happened to this point. Many times, I have seen patients who have been in chiropractic care or physical therapy for as much as two years. When asked if they are better, they say "no". I proceed with the obvious questions, "Well, why do you keep going?" They say they feel better while they are there. When I ask, "Well, doesn't it seem rather useless if you haven't been able to get back to work and do your usual activities?" They shift the responsibility and say, "That's what my doctor (or lawyer) told me to do."

There is some hope that things can change. As reported earlier, the medical director of the Labor Commission in Utah changed the rules in Utah in 1997 so that additional physical therapy could not be provided after the first six visits unless some documentation of improved function were available. This changed completely the type of therapy being carried out in the workers' compensation treatment programs in Utah. The number of physical therapy visits went down from eighteen to fourteen on average. The use of active exercise programs increased by fifty percent while the use of hot packs and massage decreased about the same amount. That shows that therapists knew what to do but they apparently thought that giving short-term relief was their job. They provided passive care until actual functional improvement was demanded and monitored. They apparently felt that, if the patient just felt better, they would eventually get better by natural healing. Not so if tissue and muscle atrophy occurs.

Recently, the State of California has limited the amount of physical therapy or chiropractic visits to twenty-four visits annually. Of course, that is not the smartest way to reduce therapy costs. On some occasions, in a complex case, many more active exercise treatments are necessary. This is true especially if an individual has failed a previous physical therapy program lasting several months and then has surgery. After surgery, it certainly is justifiable to pursue an additional therapy program which should be restorative strengthening exercises. On the basis of the ability of our physical therapy centers to document improvement by measurement of function in terms of gaining strength, range of motion and endurance as well as perceived level of function by way of the eMTAP, we have been able to convince many insurance companies to authorize therapy as long as we can demonstrate continued improvement in function. Perhaps that concept will grow.

Who Wants to Reduce the Cost of Surgery?

Unfortunately, I'm pretty cynical about the future of gradual progressive strengthening exercise as being a mainstream therapeutic endeavor. A larger consensus of physicians and insurers has to reinforce the benefits. There are so many alternatives in treatment, which are so much more financially beneficial to the physicians and therapists that simple, progressive resistance exercises probably will not gain much traction. The patient has to be induced into believing that this slow, progressive strengthening program will be of benefit. At least in the case of the scoliotic adolescent kids, the improved X-rays of diminishing curvature and the absence of stress from wearing an ugly body brace are sufficient biofeedback to keep them involved. The biofeedback of someone exercising has to be the recognition that, with absence of the exercise, their pain complaints return and, once again, they have to turn to medication or the potential for surgery. Or they can proceed with a progressive exercise program.

Well, what else is there? At this point, the total disc replacement is just emerging in America. It will become a very widely used treatment program for back pain. The amount of surgery from my view will be totally unnecessary because many of the folks with chronic back pain secondary to degenerative disc disease could be remedied by an active progressive strengthening exercise program. Nonetheless, the population, noting the success of the total hip and total knee surgery, will rapidly clamor for similar results in the total disc surgery. It will be of benefit to some but many will experience the same disability that back fusions have created. But can the health care system stand the expense?

Nearly everybody eventually gets back pain. The manufacturers and spine surgeons, however, will be very anxious to provide an opportunity for relief from back pain, even if alternatives are available to avoid the surgery. How costly will it be? I recently had a former patient who had his discs treated by a now outmoded treatment called "intradiscal electrothermal therapy (IDET)". He was wealthy but still had significant back pain. He went to Munich, Germany, and had three of his discs replaced and, fortunately, was placed on a postoperative exercise program with specialized strengthening exercise equipment. He has done quite nicely. It cost him $50,000—in 2005. In a business sense, the costs are about 1/3 more for administrative factors if the treatment has to be reimbursed from some funding agency in the United States. Any doctor's office is more than happy to take cash for treatment. By current American reimbursement levels, that surgery was cheap.

What else is there? We are gradually understanding that back pain is not the same as hip or knee arthritis. The critical joint in the case of the spine is the intervertebral disc. This is a totally different piece of biologic material than are other joints. They are made up of a specific type of cartilage, which glides nicely against its mating surface, be it the knuckles of the hand, the shoulder, the elbow, the hip, etc. The lining of the joints secretes a lubricating juice. This lining, known as the synovium, also can become inflamed, react to injury with swelling and, in that it is well innervated, become quite painful as in the case of rheumatoid arthritis or osteoarthritis. It is not the same for the disc. The nerves are only on the outside of the disc. Chemical abnormalities inside the disc are not monitored by the nervous system until they seep out to the periphery. Our own research back in the early 1970s documented that a painful disc is more acid than a nonpainful disc. We are now learning that various chemical substances can initiate a healing process for the abnormal chemical events which occur after injury in certain individuals. Unfortunately, we have no understanding why these abnormal events occur in some individuals versus others who have essentially the same injury. The answer to that question awaits considerable more insight as to the causes of pain. Nonetheless, recognizing that the disc has a chemical not just a mechanical justification for pain is a large step forward. It has been well-recognized that just the appearance of the disc being degenerated, narrowed or abnormal on MRI certainly cannot identify that particular disc as being painful. What can be done to change that process?

Therapeutic Injections, Another Simple Solution

Here, again, an unguarded moment is the event which changes the future. Years ago, while I was still working at Rancho Los Amigos, an orthopaedic resident from UCI (University of California Irvine) rotated on my program at Rancho. He didn't talk much but, when he did, he usually had something important to say. He was from a Swedish heritage and quite taciturn. His name was Bjorn Eek. After a stint in the Navy for about ten years, where he was Chief of Orthopaedics at the Naval Hospital in the Philippines, he returned to the United States and, for reasons not at all clear to anyone, became interested in injection therapy known as "prolotherapy". This concept of treatment was to try to change the chemical nature of soft-tissue injuries by injecting agents which would increase scarring. Various materials were able to do this. The safest material was Dextrose, which was in a higher concentration than sugar syrup. When injected into soft tissues, because its concentration would attract water, it would create local cellular damage and initiate a repair process. Bjorn became quite skilled at this and would often be able to resolve problems that no other treatment program, including exercise, was able to do. He gradually became knowledgeable about the abnormal chemistry within the disc and started injecting discs with dextrose as well as other natural constituents of the human intervertebral disc, such as glucosamine and chondroitin sulfate. Some of the patients actually improved and, in fact, with my support and some others, we published a paper in the *Spine*

Journal documenting a sixty percent improvement of patients who were total failures from any other sort of treatment.

Now we have a grant from a wealthy patient of Dr. Eek's to proceed into some animal work, identifying the ideal concentration of these agents. We also will be including another agent, called hyaluronic acid, which is the main component of synovial fluid, the juice that allows our joints to move so smoothly. All of these are natural components but at higher concentrations than usual for the damaged disc in which they are injected. Along with some cellulose, these injections have made a significant impact on people with painful discs and Dr. Eek is gradually improving his selection process. It is anticipated eventually that changing the internal chemistry of the disc will help. Operations to unload the disc by placing spacers between the spinous processes also will probably help. The goal, of course, is to avoid the lumbar fusion and even the total disc replacement. If a natural process can resolve the problems, this is certainly a happier solution.

In the future, nutrition will be a significant factor in trying to reduce pain. In a previous chapter, I railed against the easy remedy of opioids and other pharmacologic agents, which are highly advertised. Nutritional factors can be equally positive in the treatment of chronic pain. Often there is a state of hypersensitivity which is poorly understood. Our current label for this is "fibromyalgia syndrome" and "chronic fatigue syndrome". It appears that there is an increased degree of internal inflammation accounting for these problems. Various nutritional factors can counterbalance this internal inflammation. As a starting point, fish oil, which contains high amounts of a specific agent known as omega 3, has been demonstrated to be valuable. The future of medical care will gradually proceed into nutritional guidelines as well. Nonetheless, there will be barriers to the dissemination in the pharmaceutical industry.

As pointed out earlier, the two areas in medical school which are least well taught or at least produce medical students with the lowest competence are the areas of musculo-skeletal rehabilitation and nutrition. Once again, the ideal role of the physician is an educator in healthcare. The Latin word for "teacher" is "doctor".

The problem in the future, however, will certainly be related to the costs of medical care. With improving technology (such as the total hip replacement), success of various therapeutic maneuvers and aging population, the costs of medical care will continue to rise. How can we afford that? The U.S. has the highest health costs in the world but far from the best record in terms of infant mortality, longevity and absence of degenerative diseases. Money doesn't always buy good health. What can be done to remedy this problem?

Improving the Information Highway Should Help

Transmission of information will be a major factor in guiding the events of the future, in all of human endeavor but specifically in medical care. Consider this. A single electronic toy today contains more computing power than was available to the whole world in 1960. A lecturer at Cal Tech has estimated that humans and machines will create more information in the next three years than has been created in the past 300,000 years. Innovations are coming fast and furious. We are now witnessing the evolution and growth of less invasive surgical procedures due to better instrumentation, visualization techniques and better understanding of the precise abnormal pathology. In this environment, many innovations which are tantalizing will be tried without the justification of appropriate understanding of their role. For many years, Sweden has had a system where all total hip replacements were registered and their results were recorded and progress monitored over the years. The goal of this was to see which design was better. What has really been found out is that the role of the surgeon is more important than the specific design of the total hip. Some surgeons are not as good as others. But, we knew that. Some baseball players can't hit as well as others. Usually, the goal is to avoid surgery at all if it is a complex procedure. Then, if that fails, one should find the surgeon with the most experience and skill.

The point of all this is that the future of medical care is dependent upon dissemination of information. The problem is that there are so many sources of information that especially the unsophisticated in the particular area of interest can be swayed by incorrect information. The power of advertising is overwhelming. Think of the blitz of drug ads on television which rocketed anti-inflammatory drugs such as Vioxx and Celebrex to unheard-of sales and profits. Yet the scientific information is that these drugs were little better than well-known over the counter drugs such as Ibuprofen. That is the problem with exercise—specifically resistance training with equipment. Who's going to advertise that? What pharmacologic company or implant manufacturer will discuss exercise equipment? The manufacturers of exercise equipment have such a small market that an advertising spree does not make sense. Their profit margins are too small.

The silver lining on the horizon for this whole issue, ironically, is the cost of medical care. As the costs keep spiraling upward, it becomes less and less affordable, either to employers who have used it in the past as a mechanism to maintain worthy employees, or to the government, who more and more has taken over responsibility for medical care. Is there a solution?

Consumer-Driven Healthcare

A Harvard Business School professor, Regina Herzlinger, has crystallized the concept of solution to the high cost of medicine into the phrase "consumer-driven healthcare". She emphasizes that this is not managed care. Managed care has really not been a success. Such statistics as the fact that, in 1928, the top five percent of users accounted for fifty-two percent of healthcare costs, which remained true through 1996, at the height of the managed care solution, indicating that this has not changed the economics of medicine. Her goal is to provide information to the population and independence to seek better healthcare. She sees three strategies to achieve this. First, to integrate the many diverse sources of care around organizations focused on their needs. Centers of excellence, which she calls "focus factories", will compete with each other for say diabetic care, cardiac care, etc. This implies that these centers will take advantage of modern technology and use the computer to transfer information nearly instantly. No more lost X-rays. They will all be digitally transferred to where they are needed. No more lost charts or delayed entry into charts of lab work or consultations. All will be retained in the computer. All clinicians can access the information as soon as it is available. For complex disease problems, the multiple disciplines involved with their care will freely communicate. There are some centers already achieving portions of this.

I had my aortic aneurysm fixed at the Arizona Heart Hospital, which is one of the smoothest organizations going. It is a focus factory. It wasn't entirely paperless but far along the road. It also utilized the second component of Herzlinger's strategies to improve inefficiency and real competition and that is to insure the use of technological advances in treating chronic illness. The aneurysm was fixed by a device called a stent. This is a long, slim metal mesh tube which, when shortened, expands in diameter. Thus, it could be passed up through the femoral artery to the area of importance and then expanded to fill the aorta, obliterating the bulge of the aneurysm. It worked beautifully. I was out of the hospital in a day and back home at work the next day. Well-organized, efficient centers can carry out effective care by less costly means than a diffuse community of genralists and specialists who refer patients back and forth with associated delay in reports, scheduling, etc. By the way, I found out about the surgery and the Arizona Heart Hospital from an ad in a magazine, not from physician referral. That's consumer-driven healthcare.

Current medical practice is very inefficient. Current medicine has become so complex that it is necessary that specialists evaluate the patient and provide expertise in diagnosis and treatment when they can bring their experience to bear. However, if the patient is left to wander from office to office, costs mount. Even in current general hospital practice, serious inefficiency continues to be present. Often these are carried out for financial reasons. Recently, my son's mother-in-law developed a serious infection in her foot secondary to chronic swelling in her leg. The swelling led to problems of vascularity and it looked as if she might have to have an amputation. She required hospitalization. However, while there, she was evaluated by six different specialists as the Ping-Pong of referral of mutual back scratching occurred. Doctors often refer cases to a specialist with the anticipation that, sometime later, the specialist will refer them a case. Yet the care for this lady's problem was relatively simple. It could have been accomplished by any one of the six specialists. Merely elevation of the leg to avoid edema and giving antibiotics to control the infection would resolve the problem. One knowledgeable clinician could have handled the whole thing. That, no doubt, would have happened if this lady were in a rural area where there were few specialists who were overworked and had no desire to play Ping-Pong.

Of course, a portion of Herzlinger's concept of consumer-driven healthcare is that consumer intelligence and interest in appropriate medical care, which is efficient, will be heightened if the patient/consumer pays cash for the care. That's the way medicine was done up until the late thirties. Health insurance grew, starting just before the Second World War. Now several schemes have been proposed under the umbrella known as medical savings accounts, which are essentially mechanisms to provide insurance for catastrophic needs but systems to which funds are contributed which can be turned into healthcare at the choice of the consumer. When the money is coming out of the pocket of the consumer, efficient and effective healthcare will be demanded and made available.

Even here, my own experience confirms the reality of that. I had a total hip replacement about three years ago. As a physician, I was aware of the most experienced and effective hip surgeon in our community. He, however, tired of the numerous hoops to jump through and insufficient funding provided by Medicare, no longer took insurance and only charged his surgeon's fee for cash. I was very glad to pay it as I knew he would provide the best service and the most appropriate implant for me. It has been the case. I have had absolutely no problems with my new hip.

The third strategy that Herzlinger has advocated to reduce the cost of medicine is the concept that the healthcare system should support the patient's ability to promote their own health status and to care for themselves. This, of course, is easier said than done. Making people believe that they have some control over their health for many of the diseases that befall us in a difficult process. However, here is where such things as progressive resistance exercise programs for the treatment of chronic musculoskeletal problems can be of benefit. It's inexpensive. Its utilization awaits the enthusiastic support of the medical profession as a whole. All of us search for the easy way. It takes time to support the value of exercise on the part of the treating/teaching physician. Some breakthrough in that area has to develop. There is one possibility in the future.

If physicians, both specialists and generalists, can understand that partial ownership in an exercise center can be an enhancement to the practice, the concept may grow. Certainly, having an exercise center as part of the practice location can offset the overhead and add a different luster to the practice. That's what spine surgeon Dr. Raiszadeh has done in San Diego. It is called CORE Spinal Fitness Center. It is beginning to prosper. Certainly there are numerous exercise centers in the community, ranging from the YMCA to LA Fitness, etc. The principles of training are simple and should easily be transferred from the trainers to the patients. Unfortunately, many of these commercial centers do not have specific equipment or properly trained staff for the spine for fear of doing some damage on the occasion of progressive exercises. The reality is that the use of machines while exercising is safer than using calisthenics or exercise balls. It is difficult to communicate that, however.

So where has the unguarded moment taken us? It has been a wonderful learning process and I feel I have a significant edge in knowledge in a specific area of treatment over my colleagues. Not that it's a secret, it's just that the concept has been poorly promulgated. The unguarded moment here now at the end of the trail has become the expected moment. Now I am searching for opportunities to move the concept along. Opportunities constantly emerge and the trail will not end here. This road to understanding has been a lot of fun and I would like to do it over again. Hopefully somebody will continue to do it in the future. Perhaps he/she is reading this book now.